Daniel G. Colley

Dept. of Microbiology
and Immunology

Tulane University
School of Medicine

1968

DANIEL G. COLLEY, Ph. D.
MEDICAL SERVICE (IMMUNOLOGY)
VA HOSPITAL
NASHVILLE, TENNESSEE 37203

MANUAL OF

Experimental Statistics

PRENTICE-HALL MATHEMATICS SERIES

ALBERT A. BENNETT, EDITOR

MANUAL OF

Experimental Statistics

John E. Freund, Paul E. Livermore, Irwin Miller

Department of Mathematics & Statistical Laboratory
Arizona State University

PRENTICE-HALL, INC. | ENGLEWOOD CLIFFS, N. J.

Library of Congress Catalog Card Number: 60-11893

Current printing (last digit):

12 11 10 9 8 7 6 5 4 3

PRINTED IN THE UNITED STATES OF AMERICA

55348—C

PREFACE

THE PURPOSE of this manual is to present *in outline form* the most frequently used statistical techniques, including appropriate computing formulas and completely worked-out examples of each method. This manual is not intended as a text on statistical methods; rather it is designed to supplement the wide variety of available texts and to provide ready reference to important methods to research workers in such fields as engineering, the physical sciences, agriculture, biology, psychology, medicine.

THE AUTHORS express their appreciation and indebtedness to Professor Frederick E. Croxton and Prentice-Hall, Inc., for permission to reproduce Table I; to Professor R. A. Fisher and Messrs. Oliver and Boyd, Ltd., Edinburgh, for permission to reprint Tables III and IV from their book *Statistical Methods for Research Workers;* to Professor E. S. Pearson and the Biometrika trustees for permission to reproduce the material in Tables IV and V; to H. L. Harter (Wright Air Development Center) for permission to reproduce the material in Table VI.

John E. Freund, Paul E. Livermore, Irwin Miller

ARIZONA STATE UNIVERSITY

v

CONTENTS

PART I

Concepts and Terminology

PART I

Concepts and Terminology

Mathematical Notation

Subscripts

Subscripts are used to differentiate among observations. Thus, x_1 stands for the first observation of variable x, x_2 stands for the second observation, ..., and in general x_i stands for any one of the observations of variable x, with $i = 1, 2, 3, \ldots, n$, the total number of observations being n. For example, if 5 batches of a chemical compound are analyzed for presence of H_2O by volume, the results might be expressed as

$$x_1 = 52.1, \quad x_2 = 53.5, \quad x_3 = 51.7, \quad x_4 = 54.2, \quad x_5 = 52.9.$$

Two or more subscripts are often needed to refer, for example, to the fifth observation of the third sample as x_{53}, to the third observation obtained by the second operator with the fourth machine as x_{324} or, more generally, to the ith observation obtained with the jth treatment on the kth day as x_{ijk}.

Summations

The symbol Σ (sigma) is used to denote sums. More specifically, $\sum\limits_{i=1}^{n} x_i$ stands for the sum of the x's having the subscripts $1, 2, 3, \ldots, n$, or

$$\sum_{i=1}^{n} x_i = x_1 + x_2 + x_3 + \ldots + x_n$$

Thus, for example

$$\sum_{i=1}^{5} x_i^2 = x_1^2 + x_2^2 + x_3^2 + x_4^2 + x_5^2$$

$$\sum_{j=1}^{4} (x_j - a)^2 = (x_1 - a)^2 + (x_2 - a)^2 + (x_3 - a)^2 + (x_4 - a)^2$$

Summations on two or more subscripts represent sums consisting of all the terms obtained for all values of the subscripts. Thus,

$$\sum_{i=1}^{3} \sum_{j=1}^{2} x_{ij} = x_{11} + x_{12} + x_{21} + x_{22} + x_{31} + x_{32}$$

3

Statistical Inference

Population and sample

A *population* is any finite or infinite collection of elements, that is, individuals, items, observations, etc., under consideration in a given problem. A *sample* is part, or a subset, of a population. The basic problem of statistical inference is to arrive at generalizations concerning populations on the basis of samples. For reasons of validity in making statistical inferences, most statistical methods assume that all samples are *random*. A sample from a finite population is said to be random if each element of the population has an equal chance of being included in the sample; a sample from an infinite population is said to be random if it consists of independent observations made on the same population.

Parameter and statistic

A *parameter* is a constant describing a population, while a *statistic* is a quantity describing a sample, namely, a function of the observations. In order to distinguish between parameters and statistics, it is customary to denote the former with Greek letters and the latter with Latin letters. Thus, the mean and the standard deviation of a population are written as μ and σ, while those of a sample are written as $\bar{x}$ and s.

Probability distribution and probability density

A function $f(x)$ which gives the probability of obtaining x, the range of x being discrete, is called a *probability distribution*. Here x is a variable which denotes the possible outcomes of an experimental observation. If the range of x is continuous, $f(x)$ is called a *probability density* (or a *distribution curve*) and the area under the curve from $x = a$ to $x = b$ gives the probability that x lies between a and b.

Randomization

Randomization is the process of arranging experimental conditions so that every possible order has a known probability of occurrence. Tables of random digits and other objective devices are generally used to randomize the order of experimental conditions. Randomization is essential to the validity of most statistical analysis.

Replication

Replication is the performance of an experiment (or parts of an experiment) more than once. In so far as possible, observations constituting a given replicate should be conducted at the same time and in the same location. In many experiments replication is required to obtain an estimate of the experimental error and it increases the precision of the resulting tests and estimates.

Model

The model underlying an experimental situation is a statement, usually in the form of a mathematical equation, of the assumptions made about individual observations.

Estimation

Estimation is concerned with making inferences, generalizations, about the values of parameters. An *estimator* is a rule, a method, or a formula, for estimating a parameter. Thus, a sample mean $\bar{x}$ is frequently used as an estimator, or estimate, of a population mean μ. Instead of estimating a parameter with a single number, called a *point estimate*, it is often desirable to use an interval, called a *confidence interval*. A $(1 - \alpha)$ per cent confidence interval for a parameter π is given by a pair of statistics $\underline{\pi}$ and $\bar{\pi}$, which are such that one can assert with a probability of $1 - \alpha$ that the interval from $\underline{\pi}$ to $\bar{\pi}$ contains π.

Tests of hypotheses

A statistical hypothesis is a statement about the parameters and (or) form of a population. A test of a statistical hypothesis is a criterion which specifies for what sample results the hypothesis is to be accepted or rejected. The hypothesis to be tested is generally called the *null hypothesis, H_0,* and the hypothesis against which it is to be tested is called the *alternative hypothesis, H_1.* So long as decisions concerning the acceptance or rejection of null hypotheses are made on the basis of samples, there is always the possibility of making incorrect decisions. The following table summarizes the various situations that can arise when testing H_0 against H_1:

	Accept H_0	Accept H_1
H_0 is true	No error	Type I error
H_1 is true	Type II error	No error

The probabilities of committing a Type I and a Type II error are written as α and β, respectively; α is called the *size* of the test and $1 - \beta$ the *power* of the test. The most generally accepted procedure for selecting a "best" test of a statistical hypothesis is to fix the size and then select the test which maximizes the power.

When the primary concern of a test is to see whether the null hypothesis can be rejected, such a test is called a *test of significance.* In that case the quantity α is called the *level of significance* at which the test is being conducted. Once the level of significance is specified, the test consists of deciding on the basis of a sample whether H_0 can be rejected. If not, the null hypothesis may or may not be accepted, depending on whether a definite decision one way or the other must be reached.

Analysis of variance

An analysis of variance consists, essentially, of breaking the total variation (sum of squares) of a set of data into components which can be associated with particular sources of variation. That part of the total variation which is not attributed to a particular source is used as an estimate of chance variation, or better, as an estimate of the experimental error.

PART II

Methods

A. Inferences Concerning One or Two Means

A.1 Confidence intervals for population means

A confidence interval for the mean, μ, of a population is an interval for which one can assert with a given probability that it contains μ. If the sample size, n, is small and the population variance, σ^2, unknown, the t distribution is used to obtain confidence intervals for μ; if n is large, 30 or more, or if σ^2 is known, the normal distribution is used instead.

DATA:

$x_1, x_2, \ldots, x_i, \ldots, x_n$, where x_i is the ith observation in the given random sample.

MODEL:

$x_i = \mu + \epsilon_i$ for $i = 1, 2, \ldots, n$, where the ϵ_i are independent chance components with identical normal distributions $N(0, \sigma)$.

CALCULATIONS:

(a) Sample mean

$$\overline{x} = \frac{\sum\limits_{i=1}^{n} x_i}{n}$$

(b) Sample variance

$$s^2 = \frac{n \sum\limits_{i=1}^{n} x_i^2 - \left(\sum\limits_{i=1}^{n} x_i \right)^2}{n(n-1)}$$

(c) *Small sample* $1 - \alpha$ *confidence interval for* μ

$$\overline{x} - t_{\alpha/2} \frac{s}{\sqrt{n}} < \mu < \overline{x} + t_{\alpha/2} \frac{s}{\sqrt{n}}$$

where $t_{\alpha/2}$ is to be obtained from Table II for $n - 1$ degrees of freedom.

9

(d) *Large sample* $1 - \alpha$ *confidence interval for* μ

$$\bar{x} - z_{\alpha/2} \frac{s}{\sqrt{n}} < \mu < \bar{x} + z_{\alpha/2} \frac{s}{\sqrt{n}}$$

where $z_{\alpha/2}$ is to be obtained from Table I.

EXAMPLE:

A random sample of 14 observations of the height of a certain kind of plant gave the following results (in inches): 52.3, 48.1, 55.7, 56.8, 50.1, 49.2, 47.7, 50.8, 57.9, 52.5, 54.7, 49.6, 53.9, 56.0. Assuming that the above model is correct, the problem is to find a 95 per cent confidence interval for the true mean height of this kind of plant. Since

$$\sum_{i=1}^{14} x_i = 52.3 + 48.1 + \ldots + 56.0 = 735.3$$

$$\sum_{i=1}^{14} x_i^2 = (52.3)^2 + \ldots + (56.0)^2 = 38{,}766.33$$

Substituting these sums yields

(a) $\bar{x} = \dfrac{735.3}{14} = 52.52$

(b) $s^2 = \dfrac{14(38{,}766.33) - (735.3)^2}{14(13)} = 11.33$

and $s = 3.37$

(c) The 95 per cent confidence interval is

$$52.52 - 2.160 \frac{3.37}{\sqrt{14}} < \mu < 52.52 + 2.160 \frac{3.37}{\sqrt{14}}$$

$$50.58 < \mu < 54.47$$

where $t_{.025} = 2.160$ for 13 degrees of freedom according to Table II.

A.2 Test that a population mean equals a specified value

It is desired to test the hypothesis that the mean, μ, of a population equals some assumed or specified value μ_0. If the sample size, n, is small and the population variance, σ^2, unknown, the test is based on the t distribution; if n is large, 30 or more, or if σ^2 is known, the normal distribution is used instead (see Note 2, p. 12).

DATA:

$x_1, x_2, \ldots, x_i, \ldots, x_n$, where x_i is the ith observation in the given random sample.

MODEL:

$x_i = \mu + \epsilon_i$ for $i = 1, 2, \ldots, n$, where the ϵ_i are independent chance components with identical normal distributions $N(0, \sigma)$.

HYPOTHESES: (See Note 1, p. 12.)

One-tail tests:
(1) Null hypothesis: $\mu = \mu_0$
    Alternative hypothesis: $\mu < \mu_0$
or
(2) Null hypothesis: $\mu = \mu_0$
    Alternative hypothesis: $\mu > \mu_0$
Two-tail test:
Null hypothesis: $\mu = \mu_0$
Alternative hypothesis: $\mu \neq \mu_0$

CALCULATIONS:

(a) Sample mean

$$\bar{x} = \frac{\sum\limits_{i=1}^{n} x_i}{n}$$

(b) Sample variance

$$s^2 = \frac{n \sum\limits_{i=1}^{n} x_i^2 - \left(\sum\limits_{i=1}^{n} x_i\right)^2}{n(n-1)}$$

(c) t statistic

$$t = \frac{\bar{x} - \mu_0}{s} \sqrt{n}$$

TESTS:

One-tail tests:

(1) Reject the null hypothesis at the level of significance α if $t < -t_\alpha$; accept the null hypothesis or reserve judgment if $t \geq -t_\alpha$, where t_α is to be obtained from Table II for $n - 1$ degrees of freedom.

(2) Reject the null hypothesis at the level of significance α if $t > t_\alpha$; accept the null hypothesis or reserve judgment if $t \leq t_\alpha$, where t_α is to be obtained from Table II for $n - 1$ degrees of freedom.

Two-tail test:

Reject the null hypothesis at the level of significance α if $i < -t_{\alpha/2}$ or $t > t_{\alpha/2}$; accept the null hypothesis or reserve judgment if $-t_{\alpha/2} \leq t \leq t_{\alpha/2}$, where $t_{\alpha/2}$ is to be obtained from Table II for $n - 1$ degrees of freedom.

Note 1: What test is to be used (a one-tail test or a two-tail test) depends on the nature of the problem and what one intends to imply by rejecting the null hypothesis (see examples below).

Note 2: For large sample, $n \geq 30$, the procedure is exactly as outlined above with the sole exception that t is replaced by the standard normal deviate z and the critical values are obtained from Table I instead of Table II.

EXAMPLES:

(i) Using the data of the example of A.1, test at a level of significance of 0.10 whether the true mean height of the given kind of plant is *at least* 51 inches. Thus, if the null hypothesis is rejected it is implied that the true mean height is greater than 51 inches, and the hypotheses are

Null hypothesis: $\mu = 51$

Alternative hypothesis: $\mu > 51$

Since $\bar{x}$ and s are as on page 10, the calculations yield

(a) $\bar{x} = 52.52$

(b) $s = 3.37$

(c) $t = \dfrac{52.52 - 51}{3.37} \sqrt{14} = 1.67$

From Table II, $t_{.10} = 1.350$ for 13 degrees of freedom, and since this is less than 1.67 the null hypothesis is to be rejected. In other words, one can conclude that the true mean height of the given kind of plant is greater than 51 inches.

(ii) Using the same data, test at a level of significance of 0.10 whether the true mean of the heights of the given plants *equals* 51 inches. Thus, if the null hypothesis is rejected it is implied that the true mean height is less than or greater than 51 inches, and the hypotheses are

Null hypothesis: $\mu = 51$

Alternative hypothesis: $\mu \neq 51$

The calculations, being the same as before, yield

(a) $\bar{x} = 52.52$

(b) $s = 3.37$

(c) $t = 1.67$

and since $t_{.05} = 1.771$ for 13 degrees of freedom according to Table II, the null hypothesis cannot be rejected at a level of significance of 0.10.

A.3 Determination of sample size needed for estimating means

In planning an experiment designed to estimate a mean, the question of sample size is of major importance. The following method is useful for determining n when a prior estimate of the population standard deviation is available.

DATA:

A prior estimate of σ, even a good guess will do.

MODEL:

$x_i = \mu + \epsilon_i$ for $i = 1, 2, \ldots, n$, where the x_i are the (unknown) sample values to be obtained and the ϵ_i are independent chance components with identical normal distributions $N(0, \sigma)$.

CALCULATIONS:

If $E = |\bar{x} - \mu|$ is the maximum error to be tolerated with a degree of confidence of $1 - \alpha$, when using $\bar{x}$ as an estimate of μ, the required sample size is given by the formula

$$n = \frac{s^2 t_{\alpha/2}^2}{E^2}$$

where $t_{\alpha/2}$ must be obtained from Table II. Since t depends on n, a direct solution of this equation is impossible; however, a simple iterative solution is illustrated in the example.

EXAMPLE:

Suppose that it is desired to obtain another estimate of the plant heights referred to in A.1 so that one can assert with a probability of 0.95 that the error of this new estimate is not more than 1.5 inches. Based on the data on page 10, $s = 3.37$, and substitution into the above formula for n yields

$$n = \frac{(3.37)^2 t_{.025}^2}{(1.5)^2}$$

Since this equation cannot be solved directly, one can proceed
as follows:

(1) Try $t_{.025} = 1.96$, the value of $z_{.025}$:

$$n_1 = \frac{(11.33)(1.96)^2}{2.25} = 19.3 \quad \text{or} \quad 20$$

From Table II, $t_{.025} = 2.093$ for 19 degrees of freedom.

(2) Try $t_{.025} = 2.093$

$$n_2 = \frac{(11.33)(2.093)^2}{2.25} = 22.06 \quad \text{or} \quad 23$$

From Table II, $t_{.025} = 2.074$ for 22 degrees of freedom.

(3) Try $t_{.025} = 2.074$

$$n_3 = \frac{(11.33)(2.074)^2}{2.25} = 21.7 \quad \text{or} \quad 22$$

From Table II, $t_{.025} = 2.080$ for 21 degrees of freedom.

(4) Try $t_{.025} = 2.080$

$$n_4 = \frac{(11.33)(2.080)^2}{2.25} = 21.8 \quad \text{or} \quad 22$$

Since $n_3 = n_4$, further iteration is unnecessary and the required
sample size is $n = 22$.

A.4 Test of the equality of two means (independent samples and equal variances)

It is desired to test the hypothesis that the means of two normal populations are equal, given independent samples from the two populations and assuming that the population variances are equal.

DATA:

Sample 1: $x_{11}, x_{12}, \ldots, x_{1j}, \ldots, x_{1n_1}$
Sample 2: $x_{21}, x_{22}, \ldots, x_{2j}, \ldots, x_{2n_2}$

Here x_{ij} is the jth observation of the ith sample, the sample sizes are n_1 and n_2, respectively, and the samples are assumed to be independent.

MODEL:

$x_{ij} = \mu_i + \epsilon_{ij}$ with $i = 1, 2$ and $j = 1, 2, \ldots, n_i$.

The ϵ_{ij} are independent chance components with identical normal distributions $N(0, \sigma)$.

HYPOTHESES:

One-tail tests:
(1) Null hypothesis: $\mu_1 = \mu_2$
    Alternative hypothesis: $\mu_1 > \mu_2$
or
(2) Null hypothesis: $\mu_1 = \mu_2$
    Alternative hypothesis: $\mu_1 < \mu_2$
Two-tail test:
    Null hypothesis: $\mu_1 = \mu_2$
    Alternative hypothesis: $\mu_1 \neq \mu_2$

CALCULATIONS:

(a) Sample means

$$\bar{x}_1 = \frac{\sum\limits_{i=1}^{n_1} x_{1j}}{n_1}, \qquad \bar{x}_2 = \frac{\sum\limits_{i=1}^{n_2} x_{2j}}{n_2}$$

(b) Sample sums of squares

$$(n_1 - 1)s_1^2 = \sum_{j=1}^{n_1} x_{1j}^2 - \frac{\left(\sum\limits_{j=1}^{n_1} x_{1j}\right)^2}{n_1}$$

$$(n_2 - 1)s_2^2 = \sum_{j=1}^{n_2} x_{2j}^2 - \frac{\left(\sum\limits_{j=1}^{n_2} x_{2j}\right)^2}{n_2}$$

(c) t statistic

$$t = \frac{\bar{x}_2 - \bar{x}_1}{\sqrt{(n_1 - 1)s_1^2 + (n_2 - 1)s_2^2}} \sqrt{\frac{n_1 n_2 (n_1 + n_2 - 2)}{n_1 + n_2}}$$

TESTS:

One-tail tests:
(1) Reject the null hypothesis at the level of significance α if $t < -t_\alpha$; accept the null hypothesis or reserve judgment if $t \geq -t_\alpha$, where t_α is to be obtained from Table II for $n_1 + n_2 - 2$ degrees of freedom.
(2) Reject the null hypothesis at the level of significance α if $t > t_\alpha$; accept the null hypothesis or reserve judgment if $t \leq t_\alpha$, where t_α is to be obtained from Table II for $n_1 + n_2 - 2$ degrees of freedom.

Two-tail test:
Reject the null hypothesis at the level of significance α if $t < -t_{\alpha/2}$ or $t > t_{\alpha/2}$; accept the null hypothesis or reserve judgment if $-t_{\alpha/2} \leq t \leq t_{\alpha/2}$, where $t_{\alpha/2}$ is to be obtained from Table II for $n_1 + n_2 - 2$ degrees of freedom.

EXAMPLE:

A chemist has two mixtures of ethyl alcohol and water and wishes to determine if they contain the same percentage of alcohol. He draws 10 equal amounts from the first mixture, measures the specific gravity of each, and obtains the following results: 0.96883, 0.96751, 0.96840, 0.96796, 0.97027, 0.96871, 0.96813, 0.97001, 0.96855, 0.96863. Drawing 6 equal amounts from the second mixture, measuring the specific gravity, he obtains: 0.96859, 0.96874, 0.96749, 0.96868, 0.96751, 0.96759.

Assuming that the model of this section is appropriate, the hypothesis he wishes to test is

Null hypothesis: $\mu_1 = \mu_2$

Alternative hypothesis: $\mu_1 \neq \mu_2$

The necessary calculations are

(a) $\bar{x}_1 = \dfrac{(0.96883 + \ldots + 0.96863)}{10} = 0.96870$

$\bar{x}_2 = \dfrac{(0.96859 + \ldots + 0.96759)}{6} = 0.96810$

(b) $9s_1^2 = 9.3838035040 - \dfrac{(9.68700)^2}{10} = 6.6042 \times 10^{-6}$

$5s_2^2 = 5.6233076264 - \dfrac{(5.80860)^2}{6} = 1.9665 \times 10^{-6}$

(c) $t = \dfrac{0.96810 - 0.96870}{\sqrt{(6.6042 \times 10^{-6}) + (1.9665 \times 10^{-6})}} \sqrt{\dfrac{10 \cdot 6 \cdot 14}{16}}$

$= -1.48$

Since $t_{.025} = 2.145$ for 14 degrees of freedom and -1.48 lies between -2.145 and 2.145, the null hypothesis that there is no difference between μ_1 and μ_2 cannot be rejected at the 0.05 level of significance.

A.5 Test of the equality of two means (paired samples)

It is desired to test the hypothesis that the means of two normal populations are equal and either it cannot be assumed that the samples are independent or that the populations have equal variances. In the latter case the observations of the two samples are randomly paired.

DATA:

Sample 1: $x_{11}, x_{12}, \ldots, x_{1j}, \ldots, x_{1n}$
Sample 2: $x_{21}, x_{22}, \ldots, x_{2j}, \ldots, x_{2n}$

Here x_{ij} is the jth observation of the ith sample and the sample size is n. (If the two samples are randomly paired and the original sample sizes are unequal, n is the smaller of n_1 and n_2.)

MODEL:

$$d_j = x_{2j} - x_{1j} = \mu_2 - \mu_1 + \epsilon_j \quad \text{for } j = 1, 2, \ldots, n$$

The ϵ_j are independent chance components with identical normal distributions $N(0, \sigma)$.

HYPOTHESES:

One-tail tests:
(1) Null hypothesis: $\mu_1 = \mu_2$
   Alternative hypothesis: $\mu_1 > \mu_2$
or
(2) Null hypothesis: $\mu_1 = \mu_2$
   Alternative hypothesis: $\mu_1 < \mu_2$
Two-tail test:
Null hypothesis: $\mu_1 = \mu_2$
Alternative hypothesis: $\mu_1 \neq \mu_2$

CALCULATIONS:

(a) Mean of differences

$$\bar{d} = \frac{\sum\limits_{j=1}^{n} d_j}{n}$$

(b) Variance of differences

$$s_d^2 = \frac{n \sum\limits_{j=1}^{n} d_j^2 - \left(\sum\limits_{j=1}^{n} d_j \right)^2}{n(n-1)}$$

(c) t statistic

$$t = \frac{\bar{d}}{s_d} \sqrt{n}$$

Tests:

One-tail tests:

(1) Reject the null hypothesis at the level of significance α if $t < -t_\alpha$; accept the null hypothesis or reserve judgment if $t \geq -t_\alpha$, where t_α is to be obtained from Table II for $n-1$ degrees of freedom.

(2) Reject the null hypothesis at the level of significance α if $t > t_\alpha$; accept the null hypothesis or reserve judgment if $t \leq t_\alpha$, where t_α is to be obtained from Table II for $n-1$ degrees of freedom.

Two-tail test:

Reject the null hypothesis at the level of significance α if $t < -t_{\alpha/2}$ or $t > t_{\alpha/2}$; accept the null hypothesis or reserve judgment if $-t_{\alpha/2} \leq t \leq t_{\alpha/2}$, where $t_{\alpha/2}$ is to be obtained from Table II for $n-1$ degrees of freedom.

Note: For large samples, $n \geq 30$, see Note 2 on page 12.

Example:

Suppose it is desired to compare two different teaching methods to see if one is more effective than the other. Eleven pairs of students are selected so that the members of each pair are of approximately equal ability. (This selection is made so that s_d will be as small as possible if the null hypothesis is true.) One member of each pair is selected at random and taught by Method A and the other member is taught by Method B. At the end of a fixed period of time all the students are given the same test with the following results (students taught by Method A are listed first): Pair 1: 91 and 85, Pair 2: 72 and 78, Pair 3: 83 and 81, Pair 4:

92 and 93, Pair 5: 75 and 80, Pair 6: 76 and 82, Pair 7: 87 and 89, Pair 8: 78 and 79, Pair 9: 82 and 76, Pair 10: 86 and 88, Pair 11: 82 and 78. The hypotheses to be tested are

Null hypothesis: $\mu_1 = \mu_2$

Alternative hypothesis: $\mu_1 \neq \mu_2$

The 11 differences are $-6, 6, -2, 1, 5, 6, 2, 1, -6, 2, -4$ and the calculations yield

(a) $\bar{d} = \dfrac{(-6 + 6 - \ldots -4)}{11} = 0.45$

(b) $s_d^2 = \dfrac{11(199) - (5)^2}{11(10)} = 19.7$

    $s_d = 4.44$

(c) $t = \dfrac{0.45}{4.44} \sqrt{11} = 0.336$

Since $t_{.025} = 2.228$ for 10 degrees of freedom and 0.336 lies between -2.228 and 2.228, the null hypothesis that there is no difference between the two teaching methods cannot be rejected at the 0.05 level of significance.

B. Inferences Concerning Proportions

B.1 Confidence intervals for proportions

Suppose that a population has members which can be classified uniquely in one of two ways called, for the sake of simplicity, "success" and "failure," and that the probability of a success is θ. A confidence interval for θ is an interval for which one can assert with a given probability that it contains θ. For large samples, such confidence intervals are based on a normal curve approximation, and for small samples, they are based on special tables.

DATA:

A random sample of n observations (with or without replacement) consisting of x successes and $n - x$ failures.

MODEL:

It is assumed that sampling is either with replacement or that the population is so large that the probability of x successes in n trials is given, at least approximately, by

$$\frac{n!}{x!(n-x)!}\,\theta^x(1-\theta)^{n-x}$$

If n is large, the statistic

$$z = \frac{\dfrac{x}{n} - \theta}{\sqrt{\dfrac{\theta(1-\theta)}{n}}}$$

is distributed approximately as $N(0, 1)$.

CALCULATIONS:

(a) *Large sample* $1 - \alpha$ *confidence interval for* θ

$$\frac{x}{n} - z_{\alpha/2}\sqrt{\frac{\dfrac{x}{n}\left(1-\dfrac{x}{n}\right)}{n}} < \theta < \frac{x}{n} + z_{\alpha/2}\sqrt{\frac{\dfrac{x}{n}\left(1-\dfrac{x}{n}\right)}{n}}$$

where $z_{\alpha/2}$ is the "tail" of the standard normal distribution corresponding to an area of $\alpha/2$ in Table I.

(b) *Small sample* $1 - \alpha$ *confidence interval for* θ

If n is small (or if a less approximate result than that given in (a) is required), confidence intervals for θ may be obtained directly from Table V.

EXAMPLES:

(i) In a random sample of 250 cigarette smokers there were 60 who preferred Brand X while 190 preferred some other brand. The problem is to obtain a 95 per cent confidence interval for the true proportion of smokers preferring Brand X. Since $x/n = 60/250 = 0.24$, the calculations yield

(a) $$0.24 - 1.96\sqrt{\frac{(0.24)(0.76)}{250}} < \theta < 0.24 + 1.96\sqrt{\frac{(0.24)(0.76)}{250}}$$

$$0.187 < \theta < 0.293$$

where $z_{\alpha/2} = z_{.025} = 1.96$ was obtained from Table I.

(ii) In 20 test firings of a guided missile, 14 missiles functioned satisfactorily. The problem is to obtain a 95 per cent confidence interval for the expected proportion of satisfactory firings of this kind of missile. Using Table V and $x/n = 0.70$, the result is

(b) $$0.45 < \theta < 0.88$$

These values are obtained by marking 0.70 on the horizontal scale of Table V and proceeding vertically from this point until the pair of curves marked $n = 20$ are crossed. Drawing horizontal lines from the points where these curves are crossed to the vertical scale yields the desired 95 per cent confidence limits for θ.

B.2 *Test that a proportion equals a specified value*

It is desired to test the hypothesis that a population proportion θ equals some assumed or specified value θ_0. The method to be discussed applies to large samples and it consists of a normal curve approximation of the binomial distribution.

DATA:

A random sample consisting of x successes and $n - x$ failures.

MODEL:

The statistic

$$z = \frac{\dfrac{x}{n} - \theta}{\sqrt{\dfrac{\theta(1 - \theta)}{n}}}$$

is distributed approximately as $N(0, 1)$.

HYPOTHESES:

One-tail tests:
  (1) Null hypothesis: $\theta = \theta_0$
       Alternative hypothesis: $\theta < \theta_0$
  (2) Null hypothesis: $\theta = \theta_0$
       Alternative hypothesis: $\theta > \theta_0$
Two-tail test:
Null hypothesis: $\theta = \theta_0$
Alternative hypothesis: $\theta \neq \theta_0$

CALCULATIONS:

z statistic

$$z = \frac{\dfrac{x}{n} - \theta_0}{\sqrt{\theta_0(1 - \theta_0)/n}}$$

TESTS:

One-tail tests:
  (1) Reject the null hypothesis at the level of significance α if $z < -z_\alpha$; accept the null hypothesis or reserve judgment if $z \geq -z_\alpha$, where z_α is to be obtained from Table I.

(2) Reject the null hypothesis at the level of significance α if $z > z_\alpha$; accept the null hypothesis or reserve judgment if $z \leq z_\alpha$, where z_α is to be obtained from Table I.

Two-tail test:

Reject the null hypothesis at the level of significance α if $z < -z_{\alpha/2}$ or $z > z_{\alpha/2}$; accept the null hypothesis or reserve judgment if $-z_{\alpha/2} \leq z \leq z_{\alpha/2}$, where $z_{\alpha/2}$ is to be obtained from Table I.

EXAMPLE:

Suppose the missile mentioned in the example of Section B.1 is acceptable for military procurement if the probability of a successful flight is greater than 0.65. It is desired to know if the results of the test firings, 14 successes in 20 flights, justify procurement of the missile. (It is important to formulate the alternative hypothesis in such a manner that the rejection of the null hypothesis implies acceptance of the missile.) Thus

Null hypothesis: $\theta = 0.65$

Alternative hypothesis: $\theta > 0.65$

and suppose that the level of significance is set at 0.05. The calculations yield

$$z = \frac{\frac{14}{20} - 0.65}{\sqrt{(0.65)(0.35)/20}} = 0.47$$

and since this is less than $z_{.05} = 1.645$, the null hypothesis cannot be rejected. Thus, the results of the test firings do not justify procurement of the missile.

B.3 Determination of sample size needed for estimating proportions

Selection of the proper sample size in estimating proportions depends on the maximum error to be tolerated and the degree of confidence with which it is desired that this maximum not be exceeded. The following method is useful for determining n when no prior information about θ, the proportion to be estimated, is available.

DATA:

No prior information is assumed to be available.

MODEL:

If a random sample of size n contains x successes and $n - x$ failures, the statistic

$$z = \frac{\dfrac{x}{n} - \theta}{\sqrt{\dfrac{\theta(1 - \theta)}{n}}}$$

is distributed approximately as $N(0, 1)$.

CALCULATIONS:

If $E = |x/n - \theta|$ is the maximum error to be tolerated with a degree of confidence $1 - \alpha$, when using x/n as an estimate of θ, the required sample size is *at most*

$$n = \frac{z_{\alpha/2}^2}{4E^2}$$

where $z_{\alpha/2}$ is to be obtained from Table I.

EXAMPLE:

Suppose it is necessary to know how many test flights would be required to be at least 95 per cent confident that the error in estimating the true proportion of successful firings by means of the sample proportion will not exceed 0.15. The calculations yield

$$n = \frac{(1.96)^2}{4(0.15)^2} = 42.7 \quad \text{or} \quad 43$$

Thus, if the estimate of θ is based on a random sample of 43 observations, one can assert with a probability of 0.95 that the error will not exceed 0.15 regardless of the true value of θ.

B.4 Test of the equality of two proportions

It is desired to test the equality of two population proportions on the basis of large random samples which need not be of equal size.

DATA:

Sample 1: x_1 successes and $n_1 - x_1$ failures
Sample 2: x_2 successes and $n_2 - x_2$ failures

MODEL:

The statistic

$$z = \frac{\dfrac{x_1}{n_1} - \dfrac{x_2}{n_2}}{\sqrt{\theta(1 - \theta)\left(\dfrac{1}{n_1} + \dfrac{1}{n_2}\right)}}$$

is distributed approximately as $N(0, 1)$, where θ is the expected proportion of successes for either sample under the assumption that the two population proportions are equal.

HYPOTHESES:

One-tail tests:
(1) Null hypothesis: $\theta_1 = \theta_2 = \theta$
     Alternative hypothesis: $\theta_1 < \theta_2$
(2) Null hypothesis: $\theta_1 = \theta_2 = \theta$
     Alternative hypothesis: $\theta_1 > \theta_2$
Two-tail test:
Null hypothesis: $\theta_1 = \theta_2 = \theta$
Alternative hypothesis: $\theta_1 \neq \theta_2$

CALCULATIONS:

(a) Estimate of θ

$$\hat{\theta} = \frac{x_1 + x_2}{n_1 + n_2}$$

(b) z statistic
$$\frac{\frac{x_1}{n_1} - \frac{x_2}{n_2}}{\sqrt{\hat{\theta}(1 - \hat{\theta})\left(\frac{1}{n_1} + \frac{1}{n_2}\right)}}$$

TESTS:

One-tail tests:
(1) Reject the null hypothesis at the level of significance α if $z < -z_\alpha$; accept the null hypothesis or reserve judgment if $z \geq -z_\alpha$, where z_α is to be obtained from Table I.
(2) Reject the null hypothesis at the level of significance α if $z > z_\alpha$; accept the null hypothesis or reserve judgment if $z \leq z_\alpha$, where z_α is to be obtained from Table I.

Two-tail test:
Reject the null hypothesis at the level of significance α if $z < -z_{\alpha/2}$ or $z > z_{\alpha/2}$; accept the null hypothesis or reserve judgment if $-z_{\alpha/2} \leq z \leq z_{\alpha/2}$, where $z_{\alpha/2}$ is to be obtained from Table I.

EXAMPLE:

A manufacturer of electronic equipment wishes to subject two competing brands of transistors to an accelerated environmental test. There are 80 transistors from Manufacturer A and 50 transistors from Manufacturer B available for the test. Among them 25 of A's transistors and 21 of B's transistors failed the test. If B's transistors are less expensive than A's, it is desired to test at a level of significance of 0.05 whether there is no difference between the true proportions of failures. Thus,

Null hypothesis: $\theta_A = \theta_B$
Alternative hypothesis: $\theta_A < \theta_B$
The calculations yield

(a) $\theta = \frac{(25 + 21)}{(80 + 50)} = 0.35$

(b) $z = \frac{(0.31 - 0.42)}{\sqrt{(0.35)(0.65)(\frac{1}{80} + \frac{1}{50})}} = -1.28$

and since this is *not* less than -1.645, $z_{.05} = 1.645$, there are no grounds for rejecting the null hypothesis. Thus, the best decision is (probably) to buy the cheaper transistor.

B.5 The analysis of a contingency table

Suppose that the members of a population are classified with respect to two variables, categories or classifications, and that each variable permits two or more alternatives. It is desired to test on the basis of a sample grouped into a two-way table, or contingency table, whether the two variables are independent.

DATA:

	A_1	A_2	A_3	·	A_a	Totals
B_1	n_{11}	n_{12}	n_{13}	·	n_{1a}	$n_{1.}$
B_2	n_{21}	n_{22}	n_{23}	·	n_{2a}	$n_{2.}$
B_3	n_{31}	n_{32}	n_{33}	·	n_{3a}	$n_{3.}$
	·	·	·	·	·	·
B_b	n_{b1}	n_{b2}	n_{b3}	·	n_{ba}	$n_{b.}$
Totals	$n_{.1}$	$n_{.2}$	$n_{.3}$	·	$n_{.a}$	n

where $A_1, A_2, \ldots, A_a$ are the a categories of variable A; $B_1, B_2, \ldots, B_b$ are the b categories of variable B; and n_{ij} is the number of observations belonging to the ith category of B and the jth category of A. Also, $n_i.$ is the sum of the frequencies in the ith row, $n._j$ is the sum of the frequencies in the jth column, while n is the grand total of all observations.

MODEL:

If θ_{ij} is the probability that an observation belongs to the ith row and jth column of a contingency table, it is assumed that this probability remains constant from trial to trial and that the trials are, furthermore, independent. Also, it will be assumed that the statistic χ^2 calculated under (b) below is distributed approximately as chi-square with $(a - 1)(b - 1)$ degrees of freedom.

HYPOTHESIS:

Null hypothesis: $\theta_{ij} = \theta_i. \cdot \theta._j$ for all i and j, where $\theta_i.$ is the probability that an item belongs to the ith category of B and $\theta_{.j}$ is the probability that an item belongs to the jth category of A.

Alternative hypothesis: $\theta_{ij} \neq \theta_{i.} \cdot \theta_{.j}$ for at least one pair of values of i and j.

CALCULATIONS:

(a) Expected frequencies

$$e_{ij} = \frac{n_{i.} \cdot n_{.j}}{n}$$

(b) χ^2 statistic

$$\chi^2 = \sum_{i=1}^{b} \sum_{j=1}^{a} \frac{(n_{ij} - e_{ij})^2}{e_{ij}}$$

TEST:

Reject the null hypothesis at the level of significance α if $\chi^2 > \chi_\alpha^2$; accept the null hypothesis or reserve judgment if $\chi^2 \leq \chi_\alpha^2$, where χ_α^2 is to be obtained from Table III with $(a-1)(b-1)$ degrees of freedom.

EXAMPLE:

A business executive wished to determine the effect of previous education on the job performance of his 200 employees. Accordingly, each department manager was asked to rate his men and the following results were obtained:

| | PERFORMANCE RATING | | | |
	Outstanding	Excellent	Good	Fair
Grade school	6	10	14	8
High school	8	16	41	40
College	12	17	22	6

The calculations yield

(a) Expected frequencies

$$e_{11} = \frac{(38)(26)}{200} = 4.9$$

$$e_{12} = \frac{(38)(43)}{200} = 8.2$$

... etc.

(b) $\chi^2 = \dfrac{(6 - 4.9)^2}{4.9} + \dfrac{(10 - 8.2)^2}{8.2} + \ldots + \ldots + \dfrac{(6 - 15.4)^2}{15.4}$

$= 20.5$

and since this exceeds 12.6, the value given in Table III for $\chi^2_{.05}$ with $(3 - 1)(4 - 1) = 6$ degrees of freedom, the null hypothesis must be rejected. In other words, one can conclude that there is a dependence, a relationship, between the job performance of these employees and their prior education.

C. Inferences Concerning Variances

C.1 Confidence intervals for population standard deviations

A confidence interval for the standard deviation, σ, of a population is an interval for which one can assert with a given probability that it contains σ. The methods shown below include an exact confidence interval based on the chi-square distribution and an approximate large sample confidence interval based on the normal distribution.

DATA:

$x_1, x_2, \ldots, x_i, \ldots, x_n$, where x_i is the ith observation in the given random sample of size n.

MODEL:

$x_i = \mu + \epsilon_i$ for $i = 1, 2, \ldots, n$, where the ϵ_i are independent chance components with identical normal distributions $N(0, \sigma)$.

CALCULATIONS:

(a) Sample variance

$$s^2 = \frac{n \sum_{i=1}^{n} x_i^2 - \left(\sum_{i=1}^{n} x_i \right)^2}{n(n-1)}$$

(b) $1 - \alpha$ *confidence interval for σ*

$$\sqrt{\frac{(n-1)s^2}{\chi_2^2}} \leq \sigma \leq \sqrt{\frac{(n-1)s^2}{\chi_1^2}}$$

where $\chi_1^2 = \chi_{1-\alpha/2}^2$ with $n-1$ degrees of freedom and $\chi_2^2 = \chi_{\alpha/2}^2$ with $n-1$ degrees of freedom. The values of $\chi_{1-\alpha/2}^2$ and $\chi_{\alpha/2}^2$ are to be obtained from Table III.

(c) *Approximate large sample $1 - \alpha$ confidence interval for σ*

$$\frac{s}{1 + \frac{z_{\alpha/2}}{\sqrt{2n}}} \leq \sigma \leq \frac{s}{1 - \frac{z_{\alpha/2}}{\sqrt{2n}}}$$

where $z_{\alpha/2}$ is to be obtained from Table I.

EXAMPLE:

An optical firm purchases glass which is to be ground into lenses. Ten measurements of the index of refraction are taken of various pieces of this glass in order to find a 98 per cent confidence interval for the standard deviation of the refractive indices of the glass. These measurements are 1.589, 1.592, 1.559, 1.596, 1.561, 1.587, 1.569, 1.583, 1.590, 1.574, and the calculations yield

(a) $s^2 = \dfrac{10[(1.589)^2 + \ldots] - [1.589 + \ldots]^2}{10 \cdot 9} = 0.000178$

(b) The 98 per cent confidence interval for σ

$$\sqrt{\frac{9(0.000178)}{21.666}} \leq \sigma \leq \sqrt{\frac{9(0.000178)}{2.088}}$$

$$0.0086 \leq \sigma \leq 0.0277$$

where $\chi^2_{.99} = 2.088$ and $\chi^2_{.01} = 21.666$ for $10 - 1 = 9$ degrees of freedom were obtained from Table III.

C.2 Test that a population variance equals a specified value

It is desired to test the hypothesis that the variance, σ^2, of a normal population equals some assumed or specified value σ_0^2. The test will be based on the χ^2 statistic; for large samples, normal curve approximations may be used.

DATA:

$x_1, x_2, \ldots, x_i, \ldots, x_n$, where x_i is the ith observation of a given random sample of size n.

MODEL:

$x_i = \mu + \epsilon_i$ for $i = 1, 2, \ldots, n$, where the ϵ_i are independent chance components with identical normal distributions $N(0, \sigma)$.

HYPOTHESES:

One-tail tests:
(1) Null hypothesis: $\sigma^2 = \sigma_0^2$
    Alternative hypothesis: $\sigma^2 < \sigma_0^2$
(2) Null hypothesis: $\sigma^2 = \sigma_0^2$
    Alternative hypothesis: $\sigma^2 > \sigma_0^2$
Two-tail test:
Null hypothesis: $\sigma^2 = \sigma_0^2$
Alternative hypothesis: $\sigma^2 \neq \sigma_0^2$

CALCULATIONS:

(a) Sample variance
$$s^2 = \frac{n \sum_{i=1}^{n} x_i^2 - \left(\sum_{i=1}^{n} x_i \right)^2}{n(n - 1)}$$
(b) Chi-square statistic
$$\chi^2 = \frac{(n - 1)s^2}{\sigma_0^2}$$

TESTS:

One-tail tests:
(1) Reject the null hypothesis at the level of significance α if

$\chi^2 < \chi^2_{1-\alpha}$; accept the null hypothesis or reserve judgment if $\chi^2 \geq \chi^2_{1-\alpha}$, where $\chi^2_{1-\alpha}$ for $n - 1$ degrees of freedom is to be obtained from Table III.

(2) Reject the null hypothesis at the level of significance α if $\chi^2 > \chi^2_\alpha$; accept the null hypothesis or reserve judgment if $\chi^2 \leq \chi^2_\alpha$, where χ^2_α for $n - 1$ degrees of freedom is to be obtained from Table III.

Two-tail test:

Reject the null hypothesis at the level of significance α if $\chi^2 < \chi^2_{1-\alpha/2}$ or $\chi^2 > \chi^2_{\alpha/2}$; accept the null hypothesis or reserve judgment if $\chi^2_{1-\alpha/2} \leq \chi^2 \leq \chi^2_{\alpha/2}$, where $\chi^2_{1-\alpha/2}$ and $\chi^2_{\alpha/2}$ for $n - 1$ degrees of freedom are to be obtained from Table III.

Note: For large samples, $n \geq 30$, the z statistic

$$z = \frac{s - \sigma_0}{s} \sqrt{2n}$$

may be used instead of χ^2. The tests are similar to those outlined above with χ^2 replaced by z and the critical values obtained from Table I instead of Table III.

EXAMPLE:

Suppose the glass mentioned in the example of C.1 must have a uniform index of refraction to be acceptable; the standard deviation of the index of refraction of the glass must not exceed 0.008. Thus, the hypotheses are

Null hypothesis: $\sigma^2 = (0.008)^2$

Alternative hypothesis: $\sigma^2 > (0.008)^2$

From page 34 it is known that

(a) $s^2 = 0.000178$

and hence

(b) $\chi^2 = \dfrac{9(0.000178)}{(0.008)^2} = 25.03$

Using a level of significance of 0.01, Table III yields $\chi^2_{.01} = 21.666$ for 9 degrees of freedom, and since $25.03 > 21.666$, the null hypothesis must be rejected. It may be concluded that the true standard deviation exceeds 0.008 and that the glass is not acceptable.

C.3 Test of the equality of two variances

The t test for the equality of two means requires as one of its assumptions that the population variances are equal. The following method enables one to test this assumption when two independent samples, not necessarily of equal size, are available.

DATA:

Sample 1: $x_{11}, x_{12}, \ldots, x_{1j}, \ldots, x_{1n_1}$
Sample 2: $x_{21}, x_{23}, \ldots, x_{2j}, \ldots, x_{2n_2}$

Here x_{ij} is the jth observation of the ith sample, the sample sizes are n_1 and n_2, and the samples are assumed to be independent.

MODEL:

$x_{ij} = \mu_i + \epsilon_{ij}$ with $i = 1, 2$ and $j = 1, 2, \ldots, n_i$. The ϵ_{ij} are independent chance components with identical normal distributions $N(0, \sigma_i)$.

HYPOTHESES:

One-tail tests:
(1) Null hypothesis: $\sigma_1^2 = \sigma_2^2$
    Alternative hypothesis: $\sigma_1^2 < \sigma_2^2$
(2) Null hypothesis: $\sigma_1^2 = \sigma_2^2$
    Alternative hypothesis: $\sigma_1^2 > \sigma_2^2$
Two-tail test:
Null hypothesis: $\sigma_1^2 = \sigma_2^2$
Alternative hypothesis: $\sigma_1^2 \neq \sigma_2^2$

CALCULATIONS:

(a) Sample variances

$$s_1^2 = \frac{n_1 \sum\limits_{j=1}^{n_1} x_{1j}^2 - \left(\sum\limits_{j=1}^{n_1} x_{1j} \right)^2}{n_1(1 - n_1)}$$

$$s_2^2 = \frac{n_2 \sum\limits_{j=1}^{n_2} x_{2j}^2 - \left(\sum\limits_{j=1}^{n_2} x_{2j} \right)^2}{n_2(1 - n_2)}$$

(b) F statistic

For one-tail test (1): $F = \dfrac{s_2^2}{s_1^2}$

For one-tail test (2): $F = \dfrac{s_1^2}{s_2^2}$

For two-tail test: $F = \dfrac{larger\ variance}{smaller\ variance}$

TESTS:

One-tail tests:
(1) Reject the null hypothesis at the level of significance α if $F > F_\alpha$; accept the null hypothesis or reserve judgment if $F \leq F_\alpha$, where F_α with $n_2 - 1$ and $n_1 - 1$ degrees of freedom is to be obtained from Table IV.
(2) Reject the null hypothesis at the level of significance α if $F > F_\alpha$; accept the null hypothesis or reserve judgment if $F \leq F_\alpha$, where F_α with $n_1 - 1$ and $n_2 - 1$ degrees of freedom is to be obtained from Table IV.

Two-tail test:
If $s_1^2 > s_2^2$ reject the null hypothesis at the level of significance α if $F > F_{\alpha/2}$; accept the null hypothesis or reserve judgment if $F \leq F_{\alpha/2}$, where $F_{\alpha/2}$ with $n_1 - 1$ and $n_2 - 1$ degrees of freedom is to be obtained from Table IV. If $s_2^2 > s_1^2$ reject the null hypothesis at the level of significance α if $F > F_{\alpha/2}$; accept the null hypothesis or reserve judgment if $F \leq F_{\alpha/2}$, where $F_{\alpha/2}$ with $n_2 - 1$ and $n_1 - 1$ degrees of freedom is to be obtained from Table IV.

EXAMPLE:

In order to use the t test to decide whether the average strengths of two kinds of structural steel are the same, it is necessary to test first whether the samples come from populations with equal variances. Hence, it is desired to test on the basis of the following data (at the top of the next page) whether the variances of the two kinds of steel are the same:

TYPE 1 STEEL		TYPE 2 STEEL	
Tensile strength (psi)		*Tensile strength (psi)*	
86,200	87,300	88,300	85,800
81,000	86,300	84,400	87,300
83,700	89,800	82,700	86,100
80,800	81,100	81,300	83,600
89,900	88,300	82,000	84,500
81,200	88,800	80,400	87,400
86,600	89,900	83,200	84,700
82,700	86,500	82,800	87,500
83,100	88,000	85,500	84,900
88,500	87,400	84,800	80,800
		85,100	82,300
		82,300	80,500
		80,700	87,700
		84,200	85,300
		87,400	84,300

The hypotheses to be tested are

Null hypothesis: $\sigma_1^2 = \sigma_2^2$

Alternative hypothesis: $\sigma_1^2 \neq \sigma_2^2$

and the calculations yield

(a) $s_1^2 = \dfrac{20(147,617,510,000) - (1,717,100)^2}{20 \cdot 19} = 10,309,974$

$s_2^2 = \dfrac{30(213,151,460,000) - (2,527,800)^2}{30 \cdot 29} = 5,483,862$

(b) $F = \dfrac{10,309,974}{5,483,862} = 1.88$

According to Table IV, $F_{.05} = 1.96$ for 19 and 29 degrees of freedom and since $1.88 < 1.96$ the null hypothesis cannot be rejected at a level of significance of 0.10. Thus, it would be reasonable to go ahead with the t test for the means.

D. Curve Fitting

D.1 *Simple linear regression*

There are many problems in which it is desired to find the equation of a line giving the "best" fit to a set of paired values of two variables x and y. Predictions of a value of y can then be based upon an assumed or observed value of x. The word "best" is used here in the sense that the equation of the line is obtained by the method of least squares.

DATA:

(x_1, y_1), (x_2, y_2), . . . , (x_n, y_n), where (x_i, y_i) is the ith pair in a set of n pairs of observations.

MODEL:

$y_i = \alpha + \beta x_i + \epsilon_i$ for $i = 1, 2, \ldots, n$.

The ϵ_i are independent chance components with identical normal distributions $N(0, \sigma)$.

HYPOTHESES:

Null hypothesis: $\beta = 0$
Alternative hypothesis: $\beta \neq 0$

(This null hypothesis is equivalent to the hypothesis that there is no linear relationship, that is, no linear correlation, between x and y.)

CALCULATIONS:

(a) Estimates of α and β

$$\hat{\beta} = \frac{n\left(\sum_{i=1}^{n} x_i y_i\right) - \left(\sum_{i=1}^{n} x_i\right)\left(\sum_{i=1}^{n} y_i\right)}{n\left(\sum_{i=1}^{n} x_i^2\right) - \left(\sum_{i=1}^{n} x_i\right)^2}, \quad \hat{\alpha} = \bar{y} - \hat{\beta} \cdot \bar{x}$$

where $\bar{x}$ and $\bar{y}$ are the means of the given x's and y's.

(b) Residual variance

$$S_e^2 = \sum_{i=1}^{n} \frac{[(y_i - \bar{y}) - \hat{\beta}(x_i - \bar{x})]^2}{(n - 2)}$$

(c) t statistic

$$t = \frac{\hat{\beta}}{\sqrt{\dfrac{S_e^2}{\sum\limits_{i=1}^{n} (x_i - \bar{x})^2}}}$$

TEST:

Reject the null hypothesis at the level of significance α if $t < -t_{\alpha/2}$ or $t > t_{\alpha/2}$; accept the null hypothesis or reserve judgment if $-t_{\alpha/2} \leq t \leq t_{\alpha/2}$, where $t_{\alpha/2}$ is to be obtained from Table II for $n - 2$ degrees of freedom.

ESTIMATES:

(a) $1 - \alpha$ confidence limits for β are

$$\hat{\beta} \pm \frac{t_{\alpha/2} S_e}{\sqrt{\sum\limits_{i=1}^{n} (x - \bar{x})^2}}$$

where $t_{\alpha/2}$ is to be obtained from Table II for $n - 2$ degrees of freedom.

(b) Coefficient of correlation

$$r = \hat{\beta} \sqrt{\frac{\sum\limits_{i=1}^{n} (x_i - \bar{x})^2}{\sum\limits_{i=1}^{n} (y_i - \bar{y})^2}}$$

NOTE:

The methods of this section apply also to fit curves of the form $y = \alpha e^{\beta x}$ and $y = \alpha x^\beta$ after making logarithmic transformations. Taking the logarithm to the base e of both equations one gets

$$\ln y = \ln \alpha + \beta x$$

and $\qquad \ln y = \ln \alpha + \beta \cdot \ln x$

The first of these equations is linear in x and $\ln y$, the second is linear in $\ln x$ and $\ln y$.

EXAMPLE:

A series of tests was conducted to calibrate a tensile ring. The ring was placed upright in a tensile testing machine, known forces were applied, and the corresponding deflections were observed. In the following x stands for force in thousands of pounds and y for deflection in inches:

x	0	1	2	3	4	5	6
y	0.000	0.016	0.035	0.045	0.074	0.096	0.096

x	7	8	9	10	11	12
y	0.106	0.124	0.134	0.156	0.164	0.182

The sum of the x's is 78, the sum of their squares is 650, the sum of the y's is 1.196, the sum of their squares is 0.156338, the sum of the products $x_i y_i$ is 9.911, and n is 13. The estimated regression coefficients are

$$\hat{\beta} = \frac{13(9.911) - 78(1.196)}{13(650) - (78)^2} = 0.0150$$

$$\hat{\alpha} = 0.092 - 0.0150(6) = 0.002$$

and the equation of the least squares line is

$$y = 0.002 + 0.0150x$$

The calculations required for the residual variance are

x	$y - \bar{y}$	$\beta(x - \bar{x})$	$(y - \bar{y}) - \hat{\beta}(x - \bar{x})$
0	−0.092	−0.090	−0.002
1	−0.076	−0.075	−0.001
2	−0.057	−0.060	0.003
3	−0.047	−0.045	−0.002
4	−0.028	−0.030	0.002
5	−0.018	−0.015	−0.003
6	0.004	0.000	0.004
7	0.014	0.015	−0.001
8	0.034	0.030	0.004
9	0.042	0.045	−0.003
10	0.064	0.060	0.004
11	0.072	0.075	−0.003
12	0.090	0.090	0.000

$$S_e^2 = \frac{(-0.002)^2 + (-0.001)^2 + \ldots + (-0.003)^2 + (0.000)^2}{11}$$

$$= 0.000009$$

and
$$t = \frac{0.0150}{\sqrt{0.000009/182}} = 67.6$$

Since $t_{.025} = 2.20$ for 11 degrees of freedom and $67.6 > 2.20$, the null hypothesis is to be rejected and one can conclude that there is a significant linear relationship between the force and the corresponding deflection at the 0.05 level of significance.

Also, a 95 per cent confidence interval for β is

$$0.0150 - \frac{2.20(0.003)}{\sqrt{182}} < \beta < 0.0150 + \frac{2.20(0.003)}{\sqrt{182}}$$

or
$$0.0145 < \beta < 0.0155$$

and the coefficient of correlation is

$$r = 0.0150 \sqrt{182/0.0412} = 0.997$$

D.2 Polynomial regression

Most physical relationships between two variables can be
approximated quite adequately by a polynomial of sufficiently
high degree, at least within limited ranges of the variables under
consideration. The following illustrates how the coefficients of
such polynomials are obtained by the method of least squares;
no attempt is made to discuss tests of hypotheses concerning the
regression coefficients since this requires methods that are considerably more advanced.

DATA:

(x_1, y_1), (x_2, y_2), . . . , (x_n, y_n), where (x_i, y_i) is the ith pair in a
set of n pairs of observations.

MODEL:

$$y_i = \beta_0 + \beta_1 x_i + \beta_2 x_i^2 + \ldots + \beta_p x_i^p + \epsilon_i \quad \text{for } i = 1, 2, \ldots, n$$

The ϵ_i are independent chance components; no assumption about
their distribution is required for purposes of estimation.

CALCULATIONS:

(a) Sums of powers and products

$$\sum_{i=1}^{n} x_i, \quad \sum_{i=1}^{n} x_i^2, \quad \ldots, \quad \sum_{i=1}^{n} x_i^{2p}$$

$$\sum_{i=1}^{n} y_i, \quad \sum_{i=1}^{n} x_i y_i, \quad \sum_{i=1}^{n} x_i^2 y_i, \quad \ldots, \quad \sum_{i=1}^{n} x_i^p y_i$$

(b) Normal equations

$$\sum_{i=1}^{n} y_i = n b_0 + b_1 \sum_{i=1}^{n} x_i + b_2 \sum_{i=1}^{n} x_i^2 + \ldots + b_p \sum_{i=1}^{n} x_i^p$$

$$\sum_{i=1}^{n} x_i y_i = b_0 \sum_{i=1}^{n} x_i + b_1 \sum_{i=1}^{n} x_i^2 + \ldots + b_p \sum_{i=1}^{n} x_i^{p+1}$$

$$\cdot \quad \cdot \quad \cdot \quad \cdot \quad \cdot \quad \cdot \quad \cdot \quad \cdot \quad \cdot \quad \cdot \quad \cdot \quad \cdot$$

$$\sum_{i=1}^{n} x_i^p y_i = b_0 \sum_{i=1}^{n} x_i^p + b_1 \sum_{i=1}^{n} x_i^{p+1} + \ldots + b_p \sum_{i=1}^{n} x_i^{2p}$$

ESTIMATES:

The estimates of the β's are $\hat{\beta}_j = b_j$, for $j = 0, 1, 2, \ldots, p$, and they are obtained by simultaneously solving the $p + 1$ normal equations. If p is small, this may be done directly by elimination; if p is large, matrix methods and high-speed computing equipment may be required.

EXAMPLE:

Core drillings were made at one-foot intervals along the length of a vacuum-cast ingot, to determine how the amount of hydrogen present varied with the distance from the base of the ingot. The results were

x Core location (feet from base)	y Hydrogen (parts per million)
1	1.28
2	1.53
3	1.03
4	0.81
5	0.74
6	0.65
7	0.87
8	0.81
9	1.10
10	1.03

and an examination of the data, plotted on graph paper, shows that a parabola ($p = 2$) should provide a reasonably good fit.

The required calculations are

(a) $\displaystyle\sum_{i=1}^{10} x_i = 55, \quad \sum_{i=1}^{10} x_i^2 = 385, \quad \sum_{i=1}^{10} x_i^3 = 3025,$

$\displaystyle\sum_{i=1}^{10} x_i^4 = 24{,}037$

$\displaystyle\sum_{i=1}^{10} y_i = 9.85, \quad \sum_{i=1}^{10} x_i y_i = 51.04, \quad \sum_{i=1}^{10} x_i^2 y_i = 358.10$

(b) $\quad 9.85 = 10b_0 + 55b_1 + 385b_2$
$\quad 51.04 = 55b_0 + 385b_1 + 3025b_2$
$\quad 358.10 = 385b_0 + 3025b_1 + 25{,}333b_2$

The solution of this set of three simultaneous linear equations is

$$b_0 = 1.7842$$
$$b_1 = -0.3331$$
$$b_2 = 0.026827$$

and the equation fit to the data on core location, x, and hydrogen content, y, is

$$y = 1.7842 - 0.3331x + 0.026827x^2$$

D.3 Multiple linear regression

If a given variable depends on several other variables, this dependence can often be approximated by means of a linear equation like that of the model equation indicated below. The coefficients, the β's, are obtained by the method of least squares. Many other aspects of this topic must be omitted in this brief exposition in order not to exceed the scope of this manual.

DATA:

$(x_{11}, x_{12}, \ldots, x_{1p}, y_1), (x_{21}, x_{22}, \ldots, x_{2p}, y_2), \ldots,$
$(x_{n1}, x_{n2}, \ldots, x_{np}, y_n)$, where $(x_{i1}, x_{i2}, \ldots, x_{ip}, y_i)$ is the ith set of observations on the p independent variables, the x's, and the dependent variable, y.

MODEL:

$y_i = \beta_0 + \beta_1 x_{i1} + \beta_2 x_{i2} + \ldots + \beta_p x_{ip} + \epsilon_i$ for $i = 1, 2, \ldots, n$.
The ϵ_i are independent chance components; no assumption about their distribution is required for purposes of estimation.

CALCULATIONS:

(a) Sums and sums of products

$$\sum_{i=1}^{n} y_i, \quad \sum_{i=1}^{n} x_{ij} \quad \text{for } j = 1, 2, \ldots, p$$

$$\sum_{i=1}^{n} x_{ij}x_{ih} \quad \text{for } j, h = 1, 2, \ldots, p$$

$$\sum_{i=1}^{n} x_{ij}y_i \quad \text{for } j = 1, 2, \ldots, p$$

(b) Normal equations

$$\sum_{i=1}^{n} y_i = nb_0 + b_1 \sum_{i=1}^{n} x_{i1} + b_2 \sum_{i=1}^{n} x_{i2} + \ldots + b_p \sum_{i=1}^{n} x_{ip}$$

$$\sum_{i=1}^{n} x_{i1}y_i = b_0 \sum_{i=1}^{n} x_{i1} + b_1 \sum_{i=1}^{n} x_{i1}^2 + b_2 \sum_{i=1}^{n} x_{i1}x_{i2} + \ldots + b_p \sum_{i=1}^{n} x_{i1}x_{ip}$$

$$\cdot \quad \cdot \quad \cdot \quad \cdot \quad \cdot \quad \cdot \quad \cdot \quad \cdot$$

$$\sum_{i=1}^{n} x_{ip}y_i = b_0 \sum_{i=1}^{n} x_{ip} + b_1 \sum_{i=1}^{n} x_{i1}x_{ip} + b_2 \sum_{i=1}^{n} x_{ip}x_{i2} + \ldots + b_p \sum_{i=1}^{n} x_{ip}^2$$

ESTIMATES:

The estimates of the β's are $\hat{\beta}_j = b_j$, for $j = 0, 1, 2, \ldots, p$, and they are obtained by simultaneously solving the $p + 1$ normal equations. If p is small, this may be done directly by elimination; if p is large, matrix methods and high-speed computing equipment may be required.

EXAMPLE:

Data were collected to determine the relationship between two processing variables and the current gain of a certain kind of transistor. The results were:

y Current gain	x_1 Diffusion time (hours)	x_2 Sheet resistance (ohm-cm)
5.3	1.5	66
7.8	2.5	87
7.4	0.5	69
9.8	1.2	141
10.8	2.6	93
9.1	0.3	105
8.1	2.4	111
7.2	2.0	78
6.5	0.7	66
12.6	1.6	123

The necessary sums, sums of squares, and sums of products are

(a) $\sum_{i=1}^{n} y_i = 84.6,$ $\sum_{i=1}^{n} x_{i1} = 15.3,$ $\sum_{i=1}^{n} x_{i2} = 959$

$\sum_{i=1}^{n} x_{i1}^2 = 29.85,$ $\sum_{i=1}^{n} x_{i1}x_{i2} = 1472.9,$ $\sum_{i=1}^{n} x_{i2}^2 = 97,171$

$\sum_{i=1}^{n} x_{i1}y_i = 132.27,$ $\sum_{i=1}^{n} x_{i2}y_i = 8450.2$

and the normal equations are

(b) $84.6 = 10b_0 + 15.3b_1 + 959b_2$
$132.27 = 15.3b_0 + 29.85b_1 + 1472.9b_2$
$8450.2 = 959b_0 + 1472.9b_1 + 97,171b_2$

The solution of this set of three simultaneous linear equations is

$$b_0 = 1.700$$
$$b_1 = 0.383$$
$$b_2 = 0.064$$

and the equation giving the "best" linear relationship between y and x_1 and x_2 is

$$y = 1.700 + 0.383x_1 + 0.064x_2$$

E. Inferences Concerning More Than Two Means

E.1 *One-way analysis of variance (sample sizes equal)*

It is desired to test the hypothesis that the means of k normal populations are equal, given independent samples of size n from the k populations and assuming that the populations have equal variances.

DATA: *Totals*

Sample 1: $x_{11}, x_{12}, \ldots, x_{1j}, \ldots, x_{1n}$ T_1

Sample 2: $x_{21}, x_{22}, \ldots, x_{2j}, \ldots, x_{2n}$ T_2
            $\cdot \quad \cdot \quad \cdot \quad \cdot \quad \cdot$

Sample i: $x_{i1}, x_{i2}, \ldots, x_{ij}, \ldots, x_{in}$ T_i
            $\cdot \quad \cdot \quad \cdot \quad \cdot \quad \cdot \quad \cdot$

Sample k: $x_{k1}, x_{k2}, \ldots, x_{kj}, \ldots, x_{kn}$ $\dfrac{T_k}{T}$

Here x_{ij} is the jth observation of the ith sample, the samples are independent and of size n, T_i is the total of the observations in the ith sample, and T is the total of the observations of all k samples.

MODEL:

$$x_{ij} = \mu_i + \epsilon_{ij} \quad \text{with } i = 1, 2, \ldots, k \text{ and } j = 1, 2, \ldots, n.$$

The ϵ_{ij} are independent chance components with identical normal distributions $N(0, \sigma)$.

Note: In the model equation μ_i is sometimes replaced by $\mu + \alpha_i$ with the restriction that $\sum_{i=1}^{k} \alpha_i = 0$.

HYPOTHESES:

Null hypothesis: $\mu_1 = \mu_2 = \ldots = \mu_k$
Alternative hypothesis: at least two of the means are unequal.

CALCULATIONS:

(a) Correction term

$$C = \frac{T^2}{kn}$$

(b) Between samples sum of squares

$$\text{SSB} = \frac{\sum\limits_{i=1}^{k} T_i^2}{n} - C$$

(c) Total sum of squares

$$\text{SST} = \sum_{i=1}^{k} \sum_{j=1}^{n} x_{ij}^2 - C$$

(d) Error sum of squares

$$\text{SSE} = \text{SST} - \text{SSB}$$

(e) Analysis of variance table

Source of variation	Degrees of freedom	Sum of squares	Mean square
Between samples	$k - 1$	SSB	$\text{MSB} = \dfrac{\text{SSB}}{k-1}$
Error	$k(n-1)$	SSE	$\text{MSE} = \dfrac{\text{SSE}}{k(n-1)}$
Total	$kn - 1$	SST	

(f) F statistic

$$F = \frac{\text{MSB}}{\text{MSE}}$$

TEST:

Reject the null hypothesis at the level of significance α if $F > F_\alpha$; accept the null hypothesis or reserve judgment if $F \leq F_\alpha$. where F_α is to be obtained from Table IV for $k - 1$ and $k(n - 1)$ degrees of freedom.

ESTIMATES:

Estimates of the μ_i $\qquad \hat{\mu}_i = \dfrac{T_i}{n}$

EXAMPLE:

Suppose there are five kinds of feed, Brands A, B, C, D, and E, and that it is desired to test whether there are any differences among the average weights gained by certain animals fed with these feeds. For a certain period of time each brand is fed to 8 animals selected at random and the following weight gains (pounds) are obtained:

Brand A: 26.5, 25.2, 30.1, 27.8, 26.4, 28.8, 24.5, 29.9
Brand B: 21.8, 17.7, 22.2, 19.5, 20.2, 22.8, 21.9, 21.1
Brand C: 26.9, 27.9, 24.5, 23.0, 21.9, 26.5, 22.1, 25.6
Brand D: 17.8, 22.8, 16.2, 17.0, 23.1, 18.7, 18.1, 17.5
Brand E: 25.2, 30.9, 27.1, 20.8, 28.6, 22.4, 22.9, 30.1

The totals for the five samples are 219.2, 167.2, 198.4, 151.2, 208.0, the grand total is 944.0, and the calculations yield

(a) $\quad C = \dfrac{944.0^2}{5.8} = 22{,}278.4$

(b) $\text{SSB} = \dfrac{219.2^2 + 167.2^2 + 198.4^2 + 151.2^2 + 208.0^2}{8} -$

$\qquad\qquad\qquad\qquad\qquad\qquad 22{,}278.4 = 408.2$

(c) $\text{SST} = 26.5^2 + 25.2^2 + \ldots + 30.1^2 - 22{,}278.4 = 641.9$

(d) $\text{SSE} = 641.9 - 408.2 = 233.7$

(e) Analysis of variance table

Source of variation	Degrees of freedom	Sum of squares	Mean square
Between samples	4	408.2	102.1
Error	35	233.7	6.68
Total	39	641.9	

(f) F statistic

$$F = \frac{102.1}{6.68} = 15.3$$

According to Table IV, $F_{.01} = 3.92$ for 4 and 35 degrees of freedom and since $15.3 > 3.92$ the null hypothesis must be rejected. This means that on the average the five feeds do not produce the same gain in weight.

ESTIMATES:

The estimates of the means μ_i are

$$\hat{\mu}_1 = \frac{219.2}{8} = 27.4$$

$$\hat{\mu}_2 = \frac{167.2}{8} = 20.9$$

$$\hat{\mu}_3 = \frac{198.4}{8} = 24.8$$

$$\hat{\mu}_4 = \frac{151.2}{8} = 18.9$$

$$\hat{\mu}_5 = \frac{208.0}{8} = 26.0$$

E.2 One-way analysis of variance (sample sizes unequal)

It is desired to test the hypothesis that the means of k normal populations are equal, given independent samples of size n_i $(i = 1, 2, \ldots, k)$ from the k populations and assuming that the populations have equal variances.

DATA:

		Totals
Sample 1:	$x_{11}, x_{12}, \ldots, x_{1j}, \ldots, x_{1n_1}$	T_1
Sample 2:	$x_{21}, x_{22}, \ldots, x_{2j}, \ldots, x_{2n_2}$	T_2
	. . . .	
Sample i:	$x_{i1}, x_{i2}, \ldots, x_{ij}, \ldots, x_{in_i}$	T_i
	. . . .	
Sample k:	$x_{k1}, x_{k2}, \ldots, x_{kj}, \ldots, x_{kn_k}$	T_k
		T

Here x_{ij} is the jth observation of the ith sample, the samples are independent, T_i is the total of the n_i observations of the ith sample, and T is the grand total of the observations of all k samples.

MODEL:

$x_{ij} = \mu_i + \epsilon_{ij}$ with $i = 1, 2, \ldots, k$ and $j = 1, 2, \ldots, n_i$.

The ϵ_{ij} are independent chance components with identical normal distributions $N(0, \sigma)$. (See also note on page 50.)

HYPOTHESES:

Null hypothesis: $\mu_1 = \mu_2 = \ldots = \mu_k$
Alternative hypothesis: at least two of the means are unequal.

CALCULATIONS:

(a) Correction term

$$C = \frac{T^2}{N}$$

where $N = n_1 + n_2 + \ldots + n_k$.

(b) Between samples sum of squares

$$\text{SSB} = \sum_{i=1}^{k} \frac{T_i^2}{n_i} - C$$

(c) Total sum of squares

$$\text{SST} = \sum_{i=1}^{k} \sum_{j=1}^{n_i} x_{ij}^2 - C$$

(d) Error sum of squares

$$\text{SSE} = \text{SST} - \text{SSB}$$

(e) Analysis of variance table

Source of variation	Degrees of freedom	Sum of squares	Mean square
Between samples	$k - 1$	SSB	$\text{MSB} = \dfrac{\text{SSB}}{k - 1}$
Error	$N - k$	SSE	$\text{MSE} = \dfrac{\text{SSE}}{N - k}$
Total	$N - 1$	SST	

(f) F statistic

$$F = \frac{\text{MSB}}{\text{MSE}}$$

TEST:

Reject the null hypothesis at the level of significance α if $F > F_\alpha$; accept the null hypothesis or reserve judgment if $F \leq F_\alpha$, where F_α is to be obtained from Table IV for $k - 1$ and $N - k$ degrees of freedom.

ESTIMATES:

Estimates of the μ_i

$$\hat{\mu}_i = \frac{T_i}{n_i}$$

Example:

The following data represent the amount of tin deposited on a sheet steel surface, measured in pounds per base box. The experiment was carried out on five different tin-plating lines, A to E, with the objective of determining whether any line was depositing an abnormal amount of tin on the surface of the steel.

Line A: 0.32, 0.31, 0.24, 0.28, 0.27, 0.30, 0.25, 0.22
Line B: 0.18, 0.21, 0.25, 0.22, 0.16, 0.21
Line C: 0.25, 0.21, 0.29
Line D: 0.29, 0.28, 0.24, 0.27, 0.21, 0.23, 0.25, 0.25
Line E: 0.16, 0.19, 0.20, 0.15, 0.20, 0.18, 0.20

The totals of the five samples are 2.19, 1.23, 0.75, 2.02, 1.28, the sample sizes are 8, 6, 3, 8, 7, and the grand total is 7.47. The calculations thus yield

(a) $C = \dfrac{7.47^2}{32} = 1.7438$ since $8 + 6 + 3 + 8 + 7 = 32$.

(b) $\text{SSB} = \dfrac{2.19^2}{8} + \dfrac{1.23^2}{6} + \ldots + \dfrac{1.28^2}{7} - 1.7438 = 0.0396$

(c) $\text{SST} = 0.32^2 + 0.31^2 + \ldots + 0.20^2 - 1.7438 = 0.0639$

(d) $\text{SSE} = 0.0639 - 0.0396 = 0.0243$

(e)   Analysis of variance table

Source of variation	Degrees of freedom	Sum of squares	Mean square
Between samples	4	0.0396	0.0099
Error	27	0.0243	0.0009
Total	31	0.0639	

(f) F statistic

$$F = \frac{0.0099}{0.0009} = 11$$

According to Table IV, $F_{.01} = 4.12$ for 4 and 27 degrees of freedom and since $11 > 4.12$ the null hypothesis must be rejected. It may be concluded that the five different tin-plating lines do not deposit equal amounts of tin on a steel surface.

The estimates of the means μ_i are

$$\hat{\mu}_1 = \frac{2.19}{8} = 0.274$$

$$\hat{\mu}_2 = \frac{1.23}{6} = 0.205$$

$$\hat{\mu}_3 = \frac{0.75}{3} = 0.250$$

$$\hat{\mu}_4 = \frac{2.02}{8} = 0.252$$

$$\hat{\mu}_5 = \frac{1.28}{7} = 0.183$$

E.3 Two-way analysis of variance (one observation per cell)

It is desired to test hypotheses concerning the effects of two additive (independent) variables. The variables will be referred to as A and B, but they are often referred to as *treatments* and *blocks* or as *row effects* and *column effects*. When a two-factor experiment is used to control an extraneous variable, the design is referred to as a *randomized block design*.

DATA:

	B_1	B_2	·	B_j	·	B_b	Totals
A_1	x_{11}	x_{12}	·	x_{1j}	·	x_{1b}	$T_1.$
A_2	x_{21}	x_{22}	·	x_{2j}	·	x_{2b}	$T_2.$
	·	·	·	·	·	·	
A_i	x_{i1}	x_{i2}	·	x_{ij}	·	x_{ib}	$T_i.$
	·	·	·	·	·	·	
A_a	x_{a1}	x_{a2}	·	x_{aj}	·	x_{ab}	$T_a.$
Totals	$T_{.1}$	$T_{.2}$	·	$T_{.j}$	·	$T_{.b}$	$T_{..}$

Here x_{ij} is the observation belonging to the ith A-classification and the jth B-classification, $T_i.$ is the total of the observations in the ith A-classification, $T_{.j}$ is the total of the observations in the jth B-classification, and $T_{..}$ is the grand total of all observations.

MODEL:

$$x_{ij} = \mu + \alpha_i + \beta_j + \epsilon_{ij} \quad \begin{cases} i = 1, 2, \ldots, a \\ j = 1, 2, \ldots, b \end{cases} \text{ where } \alpha_i \text{ is called}$$

the effect of the ith A-classification, β_j the effect of the jth B-classification, with the restrictions

$$\sum_{i=1}^{a} \alpha_i = 0 \quad \text{and} \quad \sum_{j=1}^{b} \beta_j = 0$$

The ϵ_{ij} are independent chance components with identical normal distributions $N(0, \sigma)$.

HYPOTHESES:

For variable A:

Null hypothesis: $\alpha_i = 0$ for all i
Alternative hypothesis: the α_i are not all equal to 0.

For variable B:

Null hypothesis: $\beta_j = 0$ for all j
Alternative hypothesis: the β_j are not all equal to 0.

CALCULATIONS:

(a) Correction term

$$C = \frac{T_{..}^2}{a \cdot b}$$

(b) Between A-classifications sum of squares

$$\mathrm{SSA} = \frac{\sum\limits_{i=1}^{a} T_{i.}^2}{b} - C$$

(c) Between B-classifications sum of squares

$$\mathrm{SSB} = \frac{\sum\limits_{j=1}^{b} T_{.j}^2}{a} - C$$

(d) Total sum of squares

$$\mathrm{SST} = \sum_{i=1}^{a} \sum_{j=1}^{b} x_{ij}^2 - C$$

(e) Error sum of squares

$$\mathrm{SSE} = \mathrm{SST} - \mathrm{SSA} - \mathrm{SSB}$$

(f) Analysis of variance table

Source of variation	Degrees of freedom	Sum of squares	Mean square
Between A's	$a - 1$	SSA	$\text{MSA} = \dfrac{\text{SSA}}{a - 1}$
Between B's	$b - 1$	SSB	$\text{MSB} = \dfrac{\text{SSB}}{b - 1}$
Error	$(a - 1)(b - 1)$	SSE	$\text{MSE} = \dfrac{\text{SSE}}{(a - 1)(b - 1)}$
Total	$ab - 1$	SST	

(g) F statistics

$$F_A = \frac{\text{MSA}}{\text{MSE}}$$

$$F_B = \frac{\text{MSB}}{\text{MSE}}$$

TESTS:

For variable A: Reject the null hypothesis at the level of significance α if $F_A > F_\alpha$; accept the null hypothesis or reserve judgment if $F_A \leq F_\alpha$, where F_α is to be obtained from Table IV with $a - 1$ and $(a - 1)(b - 1)$ degrees of freedom.

For variable B: Reject the null hypothesis at the level of significance α if $F_B > F_\alpha$; accept the null hypothesis or reserve judgment if $F_B \leq F_\alpha$, where F_α is to be obtained from Table IV with $b - 1$ and $(a - 1)(b - 1)$ degrees of freedom.

ESTIMATES:

Estimate of μ

$$\hat{\mu} = \frac{T_{..}}{a \cdot b}$$

Estimates of the α_i

$$\hat{\alpha}_i = \frac{T_{i.}}{b} - \frac{T_{..}}{a \cdot b}$$

Estimates of the β_j

$$\hat{\beta}_j = \frac{T_{.j}}{a} - \frac{T_{..}}{a \cdot b}$$

EXAMPLE:

Four rockets are launched from each of three different launchers, using four different fuels. It is desired to test whether there is a difference among the fuels with reference to the resulting ranges (in nautical miles) on the basis of the following data:

	Launcher			
Fuel	B_1	B_2	B_3	*Totals*
A_1	58.2	56.2	65.3	179.7
A_2	49.1	54.1	51.6	154.8
A_3	60.1	70.9	39.2	170.2
A_4	75.8	58.2	48.7	182.7
Totals	243.2	239.4	204.8	687.4

The calculations yield

(a) $\quad C = \dfrac{687.4^2}{4.3} = 39,376.56$

(b) $\mathrm{SSA} = \dfrac{179.7^2 + 154.8^2 + 170.2^2 + 182.7^2}{3} - 39,376.56$

$\qquad = 157.59$

(c) $\mathrm{SSB} = \dfrac{243.2^2 + 239.4^2 + 204.8^2}{4} - 39,376.56 = 223.85$

(d) $\mathrm{SST} = 58.2^2 + 49.1^2 + \ldots + 48.7^2 - 39,376.56$

$\qquad = 1,113.42$

(e) $\mathrm{SSE} = 1,113.42 - 157.59 - 223.85 = 731.98$

(f) Analysis of variance table

Source of variation	Degrees of freedom	Sum of squares	Mean square
Between A's	3	157.59	52.53
Between B's	2	223.85	111.93
Error	6	731.98	122.00
Total	11	1,113.42	

(g) F statistics

$$F_A = \frac{52.53}{121.99} = 0.43, \qquad F_B = \frac{111.93}{121.99} = 0.92$$

Since $F_{.05} = 4.76$ for 3 and 6 degrees of freedom, and since $F_A = 0.43 < 4.76$, the null hypothesis concerning variable A cannot be rejected at a level of significance of 0.05. This implies that there are no differences in the performance of the four fuels or, at least, that the samples did not display any significant differences.

Since $F_{.05} = 5.14$ for 2 and 6 degrees of freedom, and since $F_B = 0.92 < 5.14$, the null hypothesis concerning variable B also cannot be rejected at a level of significance of 0.05. Although this was not of immediate concern, the experiment did not show significant differences in the performance of the three launchers.

The estimate of μ is

$$\hat{\mu} = \frac{687.4}{12} = 57.3$$

the estimates of the α_i are

$$\hat{\alpha}_1 = \frac{179.7}{3} - 57.3 = \quad 2.6$$

$$\hat{\alpha}_2 = \frac{154.8}{3} - 57.3 = -5.7$$

$$\hat{\alpha}_3 = \frac{170.2}{3} - 57.3 = -0.6$$

$$\hat{\alpha}_4 = \frac{182.7}{3} - 57.3 = \quad 3.6$$

and the estimates of the β_j are

$$\hat{\beta}_1 = \frac{243.2}{4} - 57.3 = \quad 3.5$$

$$\hat{\beta}_2 = \frac{239.4}{4} - 57.3 = \quad 2.5$$

$$\hat{\beta}_3 = \frac{204.8}{4} - 57.3 = -6.1$$

E.4 *Two-way analysis of variance (n observations per cell)*

It is desired to test hypotheses concerning two variables and their interaction on the basis of n observations for all combinations of A- and B-classifications. It is assumed that the n observations per cell are not "replicates," that is, the entire $a \times b$ experiment is not performed on n separate occasions or in n different blocks. If the latter is the case, the method of analysis is as in Section E.5.

DATA:

	B_1	B_2	·	B_j	·	B_b	Totals
	x_{111}	x_{121}	·	x_{1j1}	·	x_{1b1}	
	x_{112}	x_{122}		x_{1j2}		x_{1b2}	
A_1	·	·	·	·	·	·	$T_{1..}$
	·	·		·		·	
	x_{11n}	x_{12n}		x_{1jn}		x_{1bn}	
	x_{211}	x_{221}		x_{2j1}		x_{2b1}	
	x_{212}	x_{222}	·	x_{2j2}	·	x_{2b2}	
A_2	·	·		·		·	$T_{2..}$
	·	·		·		·	
	x_{21n}	x_{22n}		x_{2jn}		x_{2bn}	
	·	·	·	·	·	·	
	x_{i11}	x_{i21}	·	x_{ij1}	·	x_{ib1}	
	x_{i12}	x_{i22}	·	x_{ij2}	·	x_{ib2}	
A_i	·	·	·	·	·	·	$T_{i..}$
	x_{i1n}	x_{i2n}		x_{ijn}		x_{ibn}	
	·	·	·	·	·	·	
	x_{a11}	x_{a21}	·	x_{aj1}	·	x_{ab1}	
	x_{a12}	x_{a22}	·	x_{aj2}	·	x_{ab2}	
A_a	·	·	·	·	·	·	$T_{a..}$
	·	·		·		·	
	x_{a1n}	x_{a2n}		x_{ajn}		x_{abn}	
Totals	$T_{.1.}$	$T_{.2.}$		$T_{.j.}$		$T_{.b.}$	$T_{...}$

Here x_{ijk} is the kth observation in the ith A-classification and the jth B-classification, $T_{i..}$ is the total of all observations in the ith A-classification, $T_{.j.}$ is the total of all observations in the jth B-classification, $T_{ij.}$ is the total of all observations in the ith A-classification *and* the jth B-classification, and $T_{...}$ is the total of all observations.

MODEL:

$$x_{ijk} = \mu + \alpha_i + \beta_j + \gamma_{ij} + \epsilon_{ijk} \quad \begin{cases} i = 1, 2, \ldots, a \\ j = 1, 2, \ldots, b \\ k = 1, 2, \ldots, n \end{cases} \text{ where } \alpha_i \text{ is}$$

the effect of the ith A-classification, β_j is the effect of the jth B-classification, γ_{ij} is the interaction between the ith A-classification and jth B-classification, with the restrictions

$$\sum_{i=1}^{a} \alpha_i = 0 \quad \sum_{j=1}^{b} \beta_j = 0 \quad \sum_{i=1}^{a} \sum_{j=1}^{b} \gamma_{ij} = 0$$

The ϵ_{ijk} are independent chance components with identical normal distributions $N(0, \sigma)$.

HYPOTHESES:

For variable A:
Null hypothesis: $\alpha_i = 0$ for all i
Alternative hypothesis: the α_i are not all equal to 0.
For variable B:
Null hypothesis: $\beta_j = 0$ for all j
Alternative hypothesis: the β_j are not all equal to 0.
For interaction:
Null hypothesis: $\gamma_{ij} = 0$ for all i and j
Alternative hypothesis: the γ_{ij} are not all equal to 0.

CALCULATIONS:

(a) Correction term

$$C = \frac{T_{...}^2}{a \cdot b \cdot n}$$

(b) Between A's sum of squares

$$\text{SSA} = \frac{\sum\limits_{i=1}^{a} T_{i..}^2}{b \cdot n} - C$$

(c) Between B's sum of squares

$$\text{SSB} = \frac{\sum\limits_{j=1}^{b} T_{.j.}^2}{a \cdot n} - C$$

(d) Between means sum of squares

$$\text{SSM} = \frac{\sum\limits_{i=1}^{a} \sum\limits_{j=1}^{b} T_{ij.}^2}{n} - C$$

(e) Interaction sum of squares

$$\text{SSI} = \text{SSM} - \text{SSA} - \text{SSB}$$

(f) Total sum of squares

$$\text{SST} = \sum\limits_{i=1}^{a} \sum\limits_{j=1}^{b} \sum\limits_{k=1}^{n} x_{ijk}^2 - C$$

(g) Error sum of squares

$$\text{SSE} = \text{SST} - \text{SSM}$$

(h) Analysis of variance table

Source of variation	Degrees of freedom	Sum of squares	Mean square
Between A's	$a - 1$	SSA	$\text{MSA} = \dfrac{\text{SSA}}{a - 1}$
Between B's	$b - 1$	SSB	$\text{MSB} = \dfrac{\text{SSB}}{b - 1}$
Interaction	$(a - 1)(b - 1)$	SSI	$\text{MSI} = \dfrac{\text{SSI}}{(a - 1)(b - 1)}$
Error	$ab(n - 1)$	SSE	$\text{MSE} = \dfrac{\text{SSE}}{ab(n - 1)}$
Total	$abn - 1$	SST	

(i) F statistics

$$F_A = \frac{\text{MSA}}{\text{MSE}}$$

$$F_B = \frac{\text{MSB}}{\text{MSE}}$$

$$F_I = \frac{\text{MSI}}{\text{MSE}}$$

Tests:

For variable A: Reject the null hypothesis at the level of significance α if $F_A > F_\alpha$; accept the null hypothesis or reserve judgment if $F_A \le F_\alpha$, where F_α is to be obtained from Table IV with $a - 1$ and $ab(n - 1)$ degrees of freedom.

For variable B: Reject the null hypothesis at the level of significance α if $F_B > F_\alpha$; accept the null hypothesis or reserve judgment if $F_B \le F_\alpha$, where F_α is to be obtained from Table IV with $b - 1$ and $ab(n - 1)$ degrees of freedom.

For interaction: Reject the null hypothesis at the level of significance α if $F_I > F_\alpha$; accept the null hypothesis or reserve judgment if $F_I \le F_\alpha$, where F_α is to be obtained from Table IV with $(a - 1)(b - 1)$ and $ab(n - 1)$ degrees of freedom.

Note: If the experiment is designed so that the n observations in each cell are not really n separate experimental setups, if they are, say, samples from the same plots, the analysis of the data is somewhat different. The interaction in the above analysis of variance table is used as an estimate of (experimental) error and the error is referred to as a sampling error. The quantity MSI in the above table is, thus, used in the denominators of F_A and F_B and there is, of course, no test for interaction.

Estimates:

Estimate of μ

$$\hat{\mu} = \frac{T_{...}}{a \cdot b \cdot n}$$

Estimates of the α_i

$$\hat{\alpha}_i = \frac{T_{i..}}{b \cdot n} - \frac{T_{...}}{a \cdot b \cdot n}$$

Estimates of the β_j

$$\hat{\beta}_j = \frac{T_{.j.}}{a \cdot n} - \frac{T_{...}}{a \cdot b \cdot n}$$

Estimates of the γ_{ij}

$$\hat{\gamma}_{ij} = \frac{T_{ij.}}{n} - \frac{T_{i..}}{b \cdot n} - \frac{T_{.j.}}{a \cdot n} + \frac{T_{...}}{a \cdot b \cdot n}$$

EXAMPLE:

The problem is the same as that of Section E.3 on page 61, but there are now 2 observations for each combination of launchers and fuels.

Launcher

Fuel	B_1	B_2	B_3	Totals
A_1	58.2 52.6	56.2 41.2	65.3 60.8	334.3
A_2	49.1 42.8	54.1 50.5	51.6 48.4	296.5
A_3	60.1 58.3	70.9 73.2	39.2 40.7	342.4
A_4	75.8 71.5	58.2 51.0	48.7 41.4	346.6
Totals	468.4	455.3	396.1	1,319.8

The calculations yield

(a) $\quad C = \dfrac{1319.8^2}{4 \cdot 3 \cdot 2} = 72{,}578.00$

(b) $\text{SSA} = \dfrac{334.3^2 + \ldots + 346.6^2}{3 \cdot 2} - 72{,}578.00 = 261.68$

(c) $\text{SSB} = \dfrac{468.4^2 + 455.3^2 + 396.1^2}{4 \cdot 2} - 72{,}578.00 = 370.98$

(d) $\text{SSM} = \dfrac{110.8^2 + 91.9^2 + \ldots + 79.9^2 + 90.1^2}{2} - 72{,}578.00$

$\qquad = 2{,}401.35$

(e)   SSI = 2,401.35 − 261.68 − 370.98 = 1,768.69

(f)   SST = $58.2^2 + 52.6^2 + \ldots + 41.4^2 - 72,578.00$
        = 2,638.30

(g)   SSE = 2,638.30 − 2,401.35 = 236.95

(h)   Analysis of variance table

Source of variation	Degrees of freedom	Sum of squares	Mean square
Between A's	3	261.68	87.23
Between B's	2	370.98	185.49
Interaction	6	1768.69	294.78
Error	12	236.95	19.75
Total	23	2638.30	

(i) $F_A = \dfrac{87.23}{19.75} = 4.42$

$F_B = \dfrac{185.49}{19.75} = 9.39$

$F_I = \dfrac{294.78}{19.75} = 14.93$

Since $F_{.05} = 3.49$ for 3 and 12 degrees of freedom and since $F_A = 4.42 > 3.49$, the null hypothesis concerning variable A must be rejected.

Since $F_{.05} = 3.88$ for 2 and 12 degrees of freedom and since $F_B = 9.39 > 3.88$, the null hypothesis concerning variable B must be rejected.

Since $F_{.05} = 3.00$ for 6 and 12 degrees of freedom and since $F_I = 14.93 > 3.00$, the null hypothesis concerning the interaction must be rejected.

The estimate of μ is

$$\hat{\mu} = \frac{1319.8}{24} = 54.99$$

Estimates of the α_i are

$$\hat{\alpha}_1 = \frac{334.3}{6} - 54.99 = 0.73$$

. . . .

Estimates of the β_j are

$$\hat{\beta}_1 = \frac{468.4}{8} - 54.99 = 3.56$$

. . . .

Estimates of the γ_{ij} are

$$\hat{\gamma}_{11} = \frac{110.8}{2} - 55.72 - 58.55 + 54.99 = -3.88$$

. . . .

E.5 Two-way analysis of variance (with replication)

Using n replications of an entire $a \times b$ experiment, that is, an experiment consisting of observations for all combinations of A- and B-classifications, it is desired to test hypotheses concerning the variables A and B, their interaction, and the effect of replication.

DATA:

The data are the same as in Section E.4 except that the third subscript in x_{ijk} now refers to the replication. Thus, x_{ijk} is an observation belonging to the ith A-classification, the jth B-classification, and the kth replication. The notation is as in Section E.4.

MODEL:

$$x_{ijk} = \mu + \alpha_i + \beta_j + \gamma_{ij} + \rho_k + \epsilon_{ijk} \quad \begin{cases} i = 1, 2, \ldots, a \\ j = 1, 2, \ldots, b \\ k = 1, 2, \ldots, n \end{cases} \text{ where}$$

the A-effects, B-effects, and interaction are defined as on page 64, and where ρ_k is the effect of the kth replication, with the restriction

$$\sum_{k=1}^{n} \rho_k = 0$$

The ϵ_{ijk} are independent chance components with identical normal distributions $N(0, \sigma)$.

HYPOTHESES:

The null hypotheses and alternative hypotheses for variable A, variable B, and interaction are the same as those given on page 64. In addition, *for replication*

Null hypothesis: $\rho_k = 0$ for all k

Alternative hypothesis: the ρ_k are not all equal to 0.

CALCULATIONS:

The formulas for C, SSA, SSB, SSM, SSI, and SST are identical with those of Section E.4. However, now (g') Between replicates sum of squares

$$SSR = \frac{\sum\limits_{k=1}^{n} T_{..k}^2}{a \cdot b} - C$$

where $T_{..k}$ is the total of all observations belonging to the kth replicate.

(h') Error sum of squares

$$SSE = SST - SSM - SSR$$

(i') Analysis of variance table

Source of variation	Degrees of freedom	Sum of squares	Mean square
Between A's	$a - 1$	SSA	$MSA = \dfrac{SSA}{a - 1}$
Between B's	$b - 1$	SSB	$MSB = \dfrac{SSB}{b - 1}$
Interaction	$(a - 1)(b - 1)$	SSI	$MSI = \dfrac{SSI}{(a - 1)(b - 1)}$
Replicates	$n - 1$	SSR	$MSR = \dfrac{SSR}{n - 1}$
Error	$(n - 1)(ab - 1)$	SSE	$MSE = \dfrac{SSE}{(n - 1)(ab - 1)}$
Total	$abn - 1$	SST	

(j') F statistics

The formulas for F_A, F_B, and F_I are the same as those on page 66. In addition

$$F_R = \frac{MSR}{MSE}$$

TESTS:

The tests for variable A, variable B, and interaction are the same as those of Section E.4. In addition, *for replication:*

Reject the null hypothesis at the level of significance α if $F_R > F_\alpha$; accept the null hypothesis or reserve judgment if $F_R \leq F_\alpha$, where F_α is to be obtained from Table IV with $n-1$ and $(n-1)(ab-1)$ degrees of freedom.

Note: In the tests for A-effects, B-effects, and interaction the number of degrees of freedom for the denominator of F is also $(n-1)(ab-1)$.

ESTIMATES:

The estimates of μ, the α_i, the β_j, and the γ_{ij} are as in Section E.4. In addition, the estimates of the ρ_k are

$$\hat{\rho}_k = \frac{T_{..k}}{a \cdot b} - \frac{T_{...}}{a \cdot b \cdot n}$$

EXAMPLE:

If, in the example of Section E.4, the first observation in each cell belongs to Replicate 1 and the second to Replicate 2, then C, SSA, SSB, SSI, SSM, and SST have the same values as before and

(g') $\text{SSR} = \dfrac{687.4^2 + 632.4^2}{12} - 72{,}578.00 = 126.04$

(h') $\text{SSE} = 2{,}638.30 - 2{,}401.35 - 126.04 = 110.91$

(i') Analysis of variance table

Source of variation	Degrees of freedom	Sum of squares	Mean square
Between A's	3	261.68	87.23
Between B's	2	370.98	185.49
Interaction	6	1768.69	294.78
Replicates	1	126.04	126.04
Error	11	110.91	10.08
Total	23	2638.30	

(j') $F_A = \dfrac{87.23}{10.08} = 8.65$

$F_B = \dfrac{185.49}{10.08} = 18.40$

$F_I = \dfrac{294.78}{10.08} = 29.24$

$F_R = \dfrac{126.04}{10.08} = 12.50$

Since $F_{.05} = 3.59$ for 3 and 11 degrees of freedom, $F_{.05} = 3.98$ for 2 and 11 degrees of freedom, $F_{.05} = 3.09$ for 6 and 11 degrees of freedom, and $F_{.05} = 4.84$ for 1 and 11 degrees of freedom, all four of the null hypotheses are to be rejected. (As a matter of fact, they could also have been rejected at a level of significance of 0.01.)

Note: It is interesting to observe that the effects of the launchers and fuels were not apparent from the first replicate, the data used in the example of Section E.3, because the strong interaction was, so to speak, used as the error term. This illustrates the importance of designing experiments enabling one to measure interactions when there is the possibility that they exist.

In addition to the estimates of μ, the α_i, the β_j, and the γ_{ij}, the estimates of the ρ_k are

$$\hat{\rho}_1 = \frac{687.4}{12} - 54.99 = 2.29$$

$$\hat{\rho}_2 = \frac{632.4}{12} - 54.99 = -2.29$$

E.6 *Multiple comparisons (Duncan's multiple range test)*

If in an analysis of variance there is a significant difference among several means, it is often desirable to know what mean, or set of means, differs significantly from what other mean, or set of means. Several methods have been proposed for this purpose, among them the Duncan Multiple Range Test presented below.

DATA:

$\bar{x}_1, \bar{x}_2, \ldots, \bar{x}_k$ are the means of k random samples of size n and MSE is an estimate of the common variance of the populations from which the samples were obtained. (In practice, the $\bar{x}_i$ are the means of given classifications in a one-way or two-way analysis of variance and MSE is the error mean square of this analysis of variance.)

MODEL:

Those governing the analysis of variance from which the $\bar{x}_i$ and MSE are obtained are the only assumptions needed.

CALCULATIONS:

(a) Standard deviation of the sample means

$$s_{\bar{x}} = \sqrt{\text{MSE}/n}$$

(b) Least significant ranges

$$R_p = s_{\bar{x}} \cdot r_p \quad p = 1, 2, \ldots, k-1$$

where r_p is to be obtained from Table VI, p is the number of means involved in a given comparison, and the number of degrees of freedom is that of MSE.

PROCEDURE:

(1) Arrange the means according to size.
(2) Compare the difference between all pairs of adjacent means

with R_2. If such differences are less than R_2, draw lines under the corresponding pairs of means.

(3) Consider all sets of three successive means. If the difference between the two extreme means of such a set is less than R_3, draw a line under the three means.

(4) Consider all sets of four successive means. If the difference between the two extreme means of such a set is less than R_4, draw a line under the four means.

. . . . . .

$(k - 1)$ Consider all sets of $k - 1$ successive means. If the difference between the two extreme means of such a set is less than R_{k-1}, draw a line under the $k - 1$ means.

Note: A line drawn under a set of means indicates that the differences among them are not significant. Also, if a line under a set of means does not extend beyond another line, it is to be disregarded.

EXAMPLE:

The example of Section E.1 showed that there were differences in the weight gained by certain animals fed five different brands of feed. Based on 8 observations each, the mean weight gains, ordered according to size, were

Brand D	Brand B	Brand C	Brand A	Brand E
18.9	20.9	24.8	26.0	27.4

and MSE equalled 6.68 with 35 degrees of freedom. The calculations thus yield:

(a) $s_{\bar{x}} = \sqrt{6.68/8} = 0.91$

(b)

	$p = 2$	$p = 3$	$p = 4$
r_p	2.88	3.02	3.11
R_p	2.62	2.75	2.83

the values of r_p being obtained from Table VI with 35 degrees of freedom.

Comparing the various sets of means with the corresponding least significant ranges gives

(2) $20.9 - 18.9 = 2.0 < 2.62$
     $24.8 - 20.9 = 3.9 > 2.62$
     $26.0 - 24.8 = 1.2 < 2.62$
     $27.4 - 26.0 = 1.4 < 2.62$
(3) $24.8 - 18.9 = 5.9 > 2.75$
     $26.0 - 20.9 = 5.1 > 2.75$
     $27.4 - 24.8 = 2.6 < 2.75$
(4) $26.0 - 18.9 = 7.1 > 2.83$
     $27.4 - 20.9 = 6.5 > 2.83$

and, omitting redundant lines, the result is

<u>D   B</u>   <u>C   A   E</u>

This means that Brands C, A, and E produce significantly higher weight gains than Brands D and B, and that there are no significant differences among the weight gains produced, respectively, by Brands D and B and by Brands C, A, and E.

E.7 Latin squares

Latin squares are used to study the effects of three *noninteracting* variables on the basis of relatively few observations or, as in the example given below, to study the effect of one variable while eliminating variations from two sources. A Latin square is a square array in which each letter (or other symbol) appears once in each row and once in each column; different letters being used to denote different treatments. The following is an example of a Latin square of side 4:

A	B	C	D
B	C	D	A
C	D	A	B
D	A	B	C

Other Latin square arrangements may be found in Fisher, R. A., and Yates, F., *Statistical Tables*, Oliver & Boyd Ltd., Edinburgh, 1948, and other sources.

DATA:

The $x_{ij(k)}$ are r^2 observations in a Latin square of side r; the first subscript, i, indicates that the observation belongs to the ith row (the ith A-classification), the second subscript, j, indicates that the observation belongs to the jth column (the jth B-classification), and the third subscript, k, stands for the treatment. It should be noticed that for a given Latin square design k is completely determined when i and j are known. $T_{i.}$ stands for the total of the observations in the ith row, $T_{.j}$ for the total of the observations in the jth column, T_k for the total of the observations corresponding to the kth treatment, and $T_{..}$ for the grand total of all the observations.

MODEL:

$x_{ij(k)} = \mu + \alpha_i + \beta_j + \tau_k + \epsilon_{ij(k)}$, $i, j, k = 1, 2, \ldots, r$ where α_i is the ith row effect, β_j is the jth column effect, τ_k is the kth

treatment effect, and the $\epsilon_{ij(k)}$ are independent chance components
with identical normal distributions $N(0, \sigma)$. The α_i, β_j, and τ_k are
subject to the restrictions

$$\sum_{i=1}^{r} \alpha_i = 0, \quad \sum_{j=1}^{r} \beta_j = 0, \quad \sum_{k=1}^{r} \tau_k = 0$$

HYPOTHESES:

For row effects:
Null hypothesis: $\alpha_i = 0$ for all i
Alternative hypothesis: the α_i are not all equal to 0.
For column effects:
Null hypothesis: $\beta_j = 0$ for all j
Alternative hypothesis: the β_j are not all equal to 0.
For treatments:
Null hypothesis: $\tau_k = 0$ for all k
Alternative hypothesis: the τ_k are not all equal to 0.

CALCULATIONS:

(a) Correction term

$$C = \frac{T_{..}^2}{r^2}$$

(b) Between rows sum of squares

$$\text{SSR} = \frac{\sum_{i=1}^{r} T_{i.}^2}{r} - C$$

(c) Between columns sum of squares

$$\text{SSC} = \frac{\sum_{j=1}^{r} T_{.j}^2}{r} - C$$

(d) Between treatments sum of squares

$$\text{SS(Tr)} = \frac{\sum_{k=1}^{r} T_k^2}{r} - C$$

(e) Total sum of squares

$$\text{SST} = \sum_{i=1}^{r} \sum_{j=1}^{r} x_{ij(k)}^2 - C$$

(f) Error sum of squares

$$SSE = SST - SSR - SSC - SS(Tr)$$

(g) Analysis of variance table

Source of variation	Degrees of freedom	Sum of squares	Mean square
Rows	$r - 1$	SSR	$MSR = \dfrac{SSR}{r-1}$
Columns	$r - 1$	SSC	$MSC = \dfrac{SSC}{r-1}$
Treatments	$r - 1$	SS(Tr)	$MS(Tr) = \dfrac{SS(Tr)}{r-1}$
Error	$(r - 1)(r - 2)$	SSE	$MSE = \dfrac{SSE}{(r-1)(r-2)}$
Total	$r^2 - 1$	SST	

(h) F statistics

$$F_R = \frac{MSR}{MSE}$$

$$F_C = \frac{MSC}{MSE}$$

$$F_{Tr} = \frac{MS(Tr)}{MSE}$$

TESTS:

For row effects: Reject the null hypothesis at the level of significance α if $F_R > F_\alpha$; accept the null hypothesis or reserve judgment if $F_R \leq F_\alpha$, where F_α is to be obtained from Table IV with $r - 1$ and $(r - 1)(r - 2)$ degrees of freedom.

For column effects: Reject the null hypothesis at the level of significance α if $F_C > F_\alpha$; accept the null hypothesis or reserve judgment if $F_C \leq F_\alpha$, where F_α is to be obtained from Table IV with $r - 1$ and $(r - 1)(r - 2)$ degrees of freedom.

For treatments: Reject the null hypothesis at the level of significance α if $F_{Tr} > F_\alpha$; accept the null hypothesis or reserve judgment if $F_{Tr} \leq F_\alpha$, where F_α is to be obtained from Table IV with $r - 1$ and $(r - 1)(r - 2)$ degrees of freedom.

ESTIMATES:

Estimate of μ

$$\hat{\mu} = \frac{T_{..}}{r^2}$$

Estimates of the α_i

$$\hat{\alpha}_i = \frac{T_{i.}}{r} - \frac{T_{..}}{r^2}$$

Estimates of the β_j

$$\hat{\beta}_j = \frac{T_{.j}}{r} - \frac{T_{..}}{r^2}$$

Estimates of the τ_k

$$\hat{\tau}_k = \frac{T_k}{r} - \frac{T_{..}}{r^2}$$

EXAMPLE:

Four soil treatments, A, B, C, and D, were applied to 16 plots of soy beans in a Latin square design like that on page 77, and the yield of each plot was measured in bushels per acre. The purpose of the experiment is to determine the effects of the soil treatments while eliminating heterogeneity in soil fertility. The following results were obtained:

				Totals
28	18	22	33	101
19	23	30	34	106
22	30	27	24	103
26	28	26	32	112
Totals 95	99	105	123	422

and the T_k, the totals for the four treatments, are 117, 87, 99, and 119, respectively. The calculations yield

(a) $\quad C = \dfrac{422^2}{4^2} = 11{,}130$

(b) $\quad \text{SSR} = \dfrac{101^2 + 106^2 + 103^2 + 112^2}{4} - 11{,}130 = 18$

(c) $\quad \text{SSC} = \dfrac{95^2 + 99^2 + 105^2 + 123^2}{4} - 11{,}130 = 115$

(d) $\text{SS(Tr)} = \dfrac{117^2 + 87^2 + 99^2 + 119^2}{4} - 11{,}130 = 175$

(e) $\quad \text{SST} = 28^2 + 18^2 + \ldots + 32^2 - 11{,}130 = 346$

(f) $\quad \text{SSE} = 346 - 18 - 115 - 175 = 38$

(g) Analysis of variance table

Source of variation	Degrees of freedom	Sum of squares	Mean square
Rows	3	18	6.0
Columns	3	115	38.3
Treatments	3	175	58.3
Error	6	38	6.3
Total	15	346	

(h) $\quad F_R = \dfrac{6.0}{6.3} = 0.95$

$\qquad F_C = \dfrac{38.3}{6.3} = 6.08$

$\qquad F_{Tr} = \dfrac{58.3}{6.3} = 9.25$

Since $F_{.05} = 4.76$ for 3 and 6 degrees of freedom and since $F_R = 0.95 < 4.76$, the null hypothesis concerning row effects cannot be rejected.

Since $F_{.05} = 4.76$ for 3 and 6 degrees of freedom and since $F_C = 6.08 > 4.76$, the null hypothesis concerning column effects must be rejected.

Since $F_{.05} = 4.76$ for 3 and 6 degrees of freedom and since $F_{Tr} = 9.25 > 4.76$, the null hypothesis concerning the four treatments must be rejected. (It should be noted that at a level of significance of 0.01 none of the hypotheses could have been rejected.)

The experiment has thus shown that there are differences among the soil treatments and, furthermore, that soil fertility seems to vary from column to column.

The estimate of μ is

$$\hat{\mu} = \frac{422}{16} = 26.4$$

Estimates of the α_i are

$$\hat{\alpha}_1 = \frac{101}{4} - 26.4 = -1.2$$

$$\hat{\alpha}_2 = \frac{106}{4} - 26.4 = \quad 0.1$$

$$. \quad . \quad . \quad .$$

Estimates of the β_j are

$$\hat{\beta}_1 = \frac{95}{4} - 26.4 = -2.6$$

$$\hat{\beta}_2 = \frac{99}{4} - 26.4 = -1.6$$

$$. \quad . \quad . \quad .$$

Estimates of the τ_k are

$$\hat{\tau}_1 = \frac{117}{4} - 26.4 = \quad 2.8$$

$$\hat{\tau}_2 = \frac{87}{4} - 26.4 = -4.6$$

$$. \quad . \quad . \quad .$$

E.8 Analysis of covariance (one-way analysis)

Combining the methods of analysis of variance and linear regression, it is desired to test hypotheses concerning a variable A having the categories A_1, A_2, . . . , and A_α, in the presence of a continuous variable which cannot be eliminated or controlled.

DATA:

The pair of observations x_{ij} and y_{ij} is the jth pair belonging to the ith classification of variable A, that is, to A_i; x is the independent variable, y is the dependent variable, T_{x_i} is the total of the x's in the ith A-classification, T_{y_i} is the total of the y's in the ith A-classification, T_x is the total of all the x's, and T_y is the total of all the y's. The number of A-classifications is a and within each there are n pairs of observations.

MODEL:

$y_{ij} = \mu + \alpha_i + \delta x_{ij} + \epsilon_{ij} \quad \begin{cases} i = 1, 2, \ldots, a \\ j = 1, 2, \ldots, n \end{cases}$ where α_i is the effect of the ith A-classification, subject to the restriction that their sum equals 0, δ is the regression coefficient, and the ϵ_{ij} are independent chance components with identical normal distributions $N(0, \sigma)$. Also, the symbol y_{ij}' will be used for the y's adjusted for the regression on x.

HYPOTHESES:

For variable A:
Null hypothesis: $\alpha_i = 0$ for all i
Alternative hypothesis: not all of the α_i are equal to 0.

CALCULATIONS:

(a) SSB_x, SSE_x, and SST_x are to be calculated for the x's with the formulas for the one-way analysis of variance of Section E.1.

(b) SSB_y, SSE_y, and SST_y are to be calculated for the y's with the formulas for the one-way analysis of variance of Section E.1.

(c) Correction term

$$C = \frac{T_x \cdot T_y}{a \cdot n}$$

(d) Between A's sum of products

$$\text{SPB} = \frac{\sum\limits_{i=1}^{a} T_{x_i} \cdot T_{y_i}}{n} - C$$

(e) Total sum of products

$$\text{SPT} = \sum_{i=1}^{a} \sum_{j=1}^{n} x_{ij} \cdot y_{ij} - C$$

(f) Error sum of products

$$\text{SPE} = \text{SPT} - \text{SPB}$$

(g) Total sum of squares for y'

$$\text{SST}_{y'} = \text{SST}_y - \frac{(\text{SPT})^2}{\text{SST}_x}$$

(h) Error sum of squares for y'

$$\text{SSE}_{y'} = \text{SSE}_y - \frac{(\text{SPE})^2}{\text{SSE}_x}$$

(i) Between A's sum of squares for y'

$$\text{SSB}_{y'} = \text{SST}_{y'} - \text{SSE}_{y'}$$

(j) Analysis of covariance table. (Here SS_x, SS_y, SP, and $SS_{y'}$, stand, respectively, for the sums of squares of the x's, the sums of squares of the y's, the sums of products, and the sums of squares of the y''s.)

Source of variation	SS_x	SS_y	SP	$SS_{y'}$	Degrees of freedom	Mean squares
Between A's	SSB_x	SSB_y	SPB	$SSB_{y'}$	$a-1$	$\text{MSB}_{y'} = \dfrac{\text{SSB}_{y'}}{a-1}$
Error	SSE_x	SSE_y	SPE	$SSE_{y'}$	$an-a-1$	$\text{MSE}_{y'} = \dfrac{\text{SSE}_{y'}}{an-a-1}$
Total	SST_x	SST_y	SPT	$SST_{y'}$	$an-2$	

(k) F statistic

$$F = \frac{\text{MSB}_{y'}}{\text{MSE}_{y'}}$$

TEST:

For variable A: Reject the null hypothesis at the level of significance α if $F > F_\alpha$; accept the null hypothesis or reserve judgment if $F \leq F_\alpha$, where F_α is to be obtained from Table IV with $a - 1$ and $an - a - 1$ degrees of freedom.

ESTIMATES:

The estimate of the regression coefficient δ is

$$\hat{\delta} = \frac{\text{SPE}}{\text{SSE}_x}$$

EXAMPLE:

An experimenter has three different cleaning agents, A_1, A_2, and A_3, and he wishes to select the most effective agent for cleaning a metallic surface. The cleanliness of a surface is measured by its reflectivity, expressed in arbitrary units as the ratio of the reflectivity observed to that of a standard mirror surface. Analysis of covariance is used since the effect of a cleaning agent on reflectivity will depend on the original cleanliness, that is, the original reflectivity, of the surface. The experimenter obtained the following results:

A_1	Original reflectivity, x	0.50	0.55	0.60	0.35
	Final reflectivity, y	1.00	1.20	0.80	1.40
A_2	Original reflectivity, x	0.75	1.65	1.00	1.10
	Final reflectivity, y	0.75	0.60	0.55	0.50
A_3	Original reflectivity, x	0.60	0.90	0.80	0.70
	Final reflectivity, y	1.00	0.70	0.80	0.90

and the totals are $T_{x_1} = 2.00$, $T_{x_2} = 4.50$, $T_{x_3} = 3.00$, $T_x = 9.50$, $T_{y_1} = 4.40$, $T_{y_2} = 2.40$, $T_{y_3} = 3.40$, and $T_y = 10.20$.

The calculations yield:

(a) $C_x = \dfrac{9.50^2}{3 \cdot 4} = 7.52$

$\text{SSB}_x = \dfrac{2.00^2 + 4.50^2 + 3.00^2}{4} - 7.52 = 0.79$

$\text{SST}_x = 0.50^2 + 0.55^2 + \ldots + 0.70^2 - 7.52 = 1.31$
$\text{SSE}_x = 1.31 - 0.79 = 0.52$

(b) $C_y = \dfrac{10.20^2}{3 \cdot 4} = 8.67$

$\text{SSB}_y = \dfrac{4.40^2 + 2.40^2 + 3.40^2}{4} - 8.67 = 0.50$

$\text{SST}_y = 1.00^2 + 1.20^2 + \ldots + 0.90^2 - 8.67 = 0.79$
$\text{SSE}_y = 0.79 - 0.50 = 0.29$

(c) $C = \dfrac{9.50 \cdot 10.20}{3 \cdot 4} = 8.08$

(d) $\text{SPB} = \dfrac{2.00 \cdot 4.40 + 4.50 \cdot 2.40 + 3.00 \cdot 3.40}{4} - 8.08$
$= -0.63$

(e) $\text{SPT} = 0.50 \cdot 1.00 + 0.55 \cdot 1.20 + \ldots + 0.70 \cdot 0.90 - 8.08$
$= -0.80$

(f) $\text{SPE} = -0.80 - (-0.63) = -0.17$

(g) $\text{SST}_{y'} = 0.79 - \dfrac{(-0.80)^2}{1.31} = 0.30$

(h) $\text{SSE}_{y'} = 0.29 - \dfrac{(-0.17)^2}{0.52} = 0.23$

(i) $\text{SSB}_{y'} = 0.30 - 0.23 = 0.07$

(j)   Analysis of covariance table

Source of variation	SS_x	SS_y	SP	$SS_{y'}$	Degrees of freedom	Mean square
Between A's	0.79	0.50	−0.63	0.07	2	0.035
Error	0.52	0.29	−0.17	0.23	8	0.026
Total	1.31	0.79	−0.80	0.30	10	

(k) $F = \dfrac{0.035}{0.026} = 1.34$

Since $F_{.05} = 4.46$ for 2 and 8 degrees of freedom and since $F = 1.34 < 4.46$, the null hypothesis concerning variable A cannot be rejected. Thus, one cannot conclude that any one of the cleaning agents is more effective than the others. The estimate of the regression coefficient δ is

$$\hat{\delta} = \frac{-0.17}{0.52} = -0.33$$

F. Factorial Experiments

F.1 2^n *factorial experiments in complete blocks*

When the categories of variables, or "treatments," are related as levels of meaningful factors, it is generally appropriate to analyze these treatments in a factorial arrangement. In particular, when the treatments consist of combinations of n factors, each of which can take on two levels, one has the 2^n factorial series. The selection of two levels for each factor is useful in screening experiments, in which one is concerned only with the detection of linear effects. The 2^n series will be illustrated with a discussion of a 2^3 factorial; the generalization to n is immediate.

When there are $n = 3$ factors, A, B, and C, each at two levels to be called 0 and 1, there are $2^3 = 8$ observations in a complete block (replication), each observation representing a different combination of the levels of the factors, that is, a different treatment combination. With r replicates there are thus $8r$ observations in the experiment. Each treatment combination is denoted by a sequence, or product, of lower case letters; if a letter is present the corresponding factor is taken at level 1, at the higher level, and if a letter is absent the corresponding factor is taken at level 0, at the lower level. Thus, treatment combination ac is taken at the higher levels of factors A and C and at the lower level of factor B. The symbol 1 denotes the treatment combination taken at the lower level of all the factors.

It is generally convenient to arrange the treatment combinations in a standard order, which is obtained by starting with treatment combination 1, multiplying by a to obtain the next treatment combination, then multiplying these two treatment combinations by b to obtain b and ab, and then multiplying the four treatment combinations in order by c to obtain c, ac, bc, and abc. The standard order and the interpretation of each treatment combination for a 2^3 factorial are as shown on the following page.

DATA:

Treatment combination	Level of factor $A \quad B \quad C$			First replicate		rth replicate
1	0	0	0	x_{0001}	..	x_{000r}
a	1	0	0	x_{1001}	..	x_{100r}
b	0	1	0	x_{0101}	..	x_{010r}
ab	1	1	0	x_{1101}	..	x_{110r}
c	0	0	1	x_{0011}	..	x_{001r}
ac	1	0	1	x_{1011}	..	x_{101r}
bc	0	1	1	x_{0111}	..	x_{011r}
abc	1	1	1	x_{1111}	..	x_{111r}

Here x_{ijkl} is the observation taken at the ith level of A, the jth level of B, the kth level of C, in the lth replicate. The subscripts i, j, and k assume the values 0 and 1, while l assumes the values 1, 2, ..., r. The sum of all observations receiving a particular treatment combination will be symbolized by enclosing the corresponding letters in parentheses. Thus, (a) denotes the sum of all observations which receive the treatment combination a; (bc) denotes the sum of all observations which receive the treatment combination bc. The sums of the observations within the replicates will be denoted T_1, T_2, ..., and T_r.

MODEL:

$$x_{ijkl} = \mu + \alpha_i + \beta_j + \gamma_k + (\alpha\beta)_{ij} + (\alpha\gamma)_{ik} + (\beta\gamma)_{jk}$$
$$+ (\alpha\beta\gamma)_{ijk} + \rho_l + \epsilon_{ijkl} \quad \begin{cases} i, j, k = 0, 1 \\ l = 1, 2, \ldots, r \end{cases}$$

where μ is the over-all mean, α_i is the effect of the ith level of factor A, β_j is the effect of the jth level of factor B, γ_k is the effect of the kth level of factor C, $(\alpha\beta)_{ij}$ is the interaction of the ith level of A with the jth level of B, $(\alpha\gamma)_{ik}$ is the interaction of the ith level of A with the kth level of C, $(\beta\gamma)_{jk}$ is the interaction of the jth level of B with the kth level of C, $(\alpha\beta\gamma)_{ijk}$ is the interaction of the ith level of A with the jth level of B and the kth level of C, and ρ_l is the effect of the lth replicate. These parameters are subject to the restriction that the sums of the α_i, the β_j, the γ_k, and the ρ_l are equal to 0, respectively, and that the sums of the $(\alpha\beta)_{ij}$, $(\alpha\gamma)_{ik}$, . . . , are equal to 0, respectively, when summed on either subscript. The ϵ_{ijkl} are independent chance components with identical normal distributions $N(0, \sigma)$.

The following are referred to as the *main effects* and *interactions* of factors A, B, and C:

The main effect of factor A is $\alpha_1 - \alpha_0$.
The main effect of factor B is $\beta_1 - \beta_0$.
The main effect of factor C is $\gamma_1 - \gamma_0$.

The AB interaction is

$$\tfrac{1}{2}[(\alpha\beta)_{11} - (\alpha\beta)_{10} - (\alpha\beta)_{01} + (\alpha\beta)_{00}]$$

The AC interaction is

$$\tfrac{1}{2}[(\alpha\gamma)_{11} - (\alpha\gamma)_{10} - (\alpha\gamma)_{01} + (\alpha\gamma)_{00}]$$

The BC interaction is

$$\tfrac{1}{2}[(\beta\gamma)_{11} - (\beta\gamma)_{10} - (\beta\gamma)_{01} + (\beta\gamma)_{00}]$$

The ABC interaction is

$$\tfrac{1}{4}[(\alpha\beta\gamma)_{111} - (\alpha\beta\gamma)_{110} - (\alpha\beta\gamma)_{101} - (\alpha\beta\gamma)_{011} +$$
$$(\alpha\beta\gamma)_{100} + (\alpha\beta\gamma)_{010} + (\alpha\beta\gamma)_{001} - (\alpha\beta\gamma)_{000}]$$

HYPOTHESES:

Null hypotheses for main effects:

Factor A: $\alpha_1 = \alpha_0$
Factor B: $\beta_1 = \beta_0$
Factor C: $\gamma_1 = \gamma_0$

Null hypotheses for two-factor interactions:

AB interaction:

$$(\alpha\beta)_{11} + (\alpha\beta)_{00} = (\alpha\beta)_{10} + (\alpha\beta)_{01}$$

AC interaction:

$$(\alpha\gamma)_{11} + (\alpha\gamma)_{00} = (\alpha\gamma)_{10} + (\alpha\gamma)_{01}$$

BC interaction:

$$(\beta\gamma)_{11} + (\beta\gamma)_{00} = (\beta\gamma)_{10} + (\beta\gamma)_{01}$$

Null hypotheses for three-factor interaction:

ABC interaction:

$$(\alpha\beta\gamma)_{111} + (\alpha\beta\gamma)_{100} + (\alpha\beta\gamma)_{010} + (\alpha\beta\gamma)_{001}$$
$$= (\alpha\beta\gamma)_{110} + (\alpha\beta\gamma)_{101} + (\alpha\beta\gamma)_{011} + (\alpha\beta\gamma)_{000}$$

Null hypotheses for replicates:

$$\rho_1 = \rho_2 = \ldots = \rho_r$$

Alternative hypotheses: The alternative hypotheses state in each case that the equality (or at least one of the equalities) does not hold.

CALCULATIONS:

(a) Effect totals: The effect totals, indicated by means of brackets, are obtained by adding and subtracting the totals for the treatment combinations as is indicated in the following table: (The symbol $[I]$ stands for the grand total of all the observations.)

(1)	(a)	(b)	(ab)	(c)	(ac)	(bc)	(abc)	Effect totals
+	+	+	+	+	+	+	+	$[I]$
−	+	−	+	−	+	−	+	$[A]$
−	−	+	+	−	−	+	+	$[B]$
+	−	−	+	+	−	−	+	$[AB]$
−	−	−	−	+	+	+	+	$[C]$
+	−	+	−	−	+	−	+	$[AC]$
+	+	−	−	−	−	+	+	$[BC]$
−	+	+	−	+	−	−	+	$[ABC]$

Thus, for example,

$$[A] = -(1) + (a) - (b) + (ab) - (c) + (ac) - (bc) + (abc)$$

(b) Correction term

$$C = \frac{[I]^2}{r \cdot 2^3}$$

(c) Main effect sums of squares

$$\text{SSA} = \frac{[A]^2}{r \cdot 2^3}$$

$$\text{SSB} = \frac{[B]^2}{r \cdot 2^3}$$

$$\text{SSC} = \frac{[C]^2}{r \cdot 2^3}$$

(d) Interactions sums of squares

$$\text{SS(AB)} = \frac{[AB]^2}{r \cdot 2^3}$$

$$\text{SS(AC)} = \frac{[AC]^2}{r \cdot 2^3}$$

$$\text{SS(BC)} = \frac{[BC]^2}{r \cdot 2^3}$$

$$\text{SS(ABC)} = \frac{[ABC]^2}{r \cdot 2^3}$$

(e) Replication sum of squares

$$\text{SSR} = \frac{\sum\limits_{l=1}^{r} T_l^2}{2^3} - C$$

(f) Total sum of squares

$$\text{SST} = \sum_{l=1}^{r} \sum_{k=0}^{1} \sum_{j=0}^{1} \sum_{i=0}^{1} x_{ijkl}^2 - C$$

(g) Error sum of squares

$$\text{SSE} = \text{SST} - \text{SSA} - \text{SSB} - \text{SS(AB)} - \text{SSC} \\ - \text{SS(AC)} - \text{SS(BC)} - \text{SS(ABC)} - \text{SSR}$$

(h) Analysis of variance table

Source of variation	Degrees of freedom	Sum of squares	Mean square
Replications	$r-1$	SSR	$\text{MSR} = \dfrac{\text{SSR}}{r-1}$
Main effects A B C	3 1 1 1	 SSA SSB SSC	 MSA = SSA MSB = SSB MSC = SSC
Two-factor interactions AB AC BC	3 1 1 1	 SS(AB) SS(AC) SS(BC)	 MS(AB) = SS(AB) MS(AC) = SS(AC) MS(BC) = SS(BC)
Three-factor interaction ABC	1 1	 SS(ABC)	 MS(ABC) = SS(ABC)
Error	$2^3(r-1)-1$	SSE	$\text{MSE} = \dfrac{\text{SSE}}{2^3(r-1)-1}$
Total	$r \cdot 2^3 - 1$	SST	

In general, in a 2^n factorial, there are n main effects,

$$\binom{n}{2} = \frac{1}{2}\,n(n-1)$$

two-factor interactions,

$$\binom{n}{3} = \frac{1}{6}\,n(n-1)(n-2)$$

three-factor interactions, etc.

(i) *F* statistics

The *F* statistics for replication, main effects, and interactions are obtained by dividing the appropriate mean square by MSE.

TESTS:

The null hypotheses are rejected at the level of significance α if the appropriate *F* ratios exceed F_α; they are accepted or judgment is reserved if they are less than or equal to F_α. The number of degrees of freedom for main effects and interactions are 1 and $2^3(r - 1) - 1$, for replications they are $r - 1$ and $2^3(r - 1) - 1$. The appropriate values of F_α are found in Table IV.

ESTIMATES:

The estimate of μ is obtained by dividing $[I]$ by $r \cdot 2^3$. The estimates of the main effects and interactions are obtained by dividing the corresponding effect totals by $r \cdot 2^{3-1}$. The estimates of the ρ_1 are

$$\hat{\rho}_1 = \frac{T_l}{2^3} - \frac{[I]}{r \cdot 2^3}$$

EXAMPLE:

An experiment was conducted to determine the effects of certain alloying elements on the ductility of several specimens of metal. The following table summarizes the factors and their levels:

Factor		Level 0	Level 1
A	Carbon	0.2%	0.5%
B	Manganese	0.5%	1.0%
C	Nickel	0.0%	3.0%

The experiment was performed twice with the following results giving breaking strength in foot-pounds of work required to break a specimen of standard dimensions:

Treatment combination	Rep. 1	Rep. 2
1	34.6	37.5
a	46.4	42.4
b	41.8	38.0
ab	40.0	44.7
c	37.8	32.7
ac	33.2	36.2
bc	38.3	40.4
abc	46.2	43.5

and the totals are $(1) = 72.1$, $(a) = 88.8$, $(b) = 79.8$, $(ab) = 84.7$, $(c) = 70.5$, $(ac) = 69.4$, $(bc) = 78.7$, $(abc) = 89.7$, $T_1 = 318.3$, and $T_2 = 315.4$.

(a) If the effect totals are calculated as indicated on page 91, one gets, for example,

$$[A] = -72.1 + 88.8 - \ldots + 89.7 = 31.5$$

Instead, a method of Yates may be used to advantage in 2^n factorials when n is relatively large; this method is illustrated below:

Treatment combinations	Totals	(i)	(ii)	(iii)
1	72.1	160.9	325.4	633.7
a	88.8	164.5	308.3	31.5
b	79.8	139.9	21.6	32.1
ab	84.7	168.4	9.9	0.3
c	70.5	16.7	3.6	−17.1
ac	69.4	4.9	28.5	−11.7
bc	78.7	−1.1	−11.8	24.9
abc	89.7	11.0	12.1	23.9

The totals are arranged in standard order and the column marked (i) is obtained by adding successive pairs and then subtracting successive pairs. Thus,

$$72.1 + 88.8 = 160.9$$
$$\cdots\cdots \qquad \cdots$$
$$78.7 + 89.7 = 168.4$$
and
$$88.8 - 72.1 = 16.7$$
$$\cdots\cdots \qquad \cdots$$
$$89.7 - 78.7 = 11.0$$

It should be noted that the first total in each pair is subtracted from the second. The entries in column (ii) are obtained by performing the same operations on the entries of column (i); and the entries in column (iii), the effect totals in standard order, are obtained by performing the same operation on the entries of column (ii).

Calculations (b) through (g) yield

$$C = \frac{633.7^2}{16} = 25,098.48$$

$$SSA = \frac{31.5^2}{16} = 62.02$$

$$SSB = \frac{32.1^2}{16} = 64.40$$

$$SSC = \frac{(-17.1)^2}{16} = 18.28$$

$$SS(AB) = \frac{0.3^2}{16} = 0.01$$

$$SS(AC) = \frac{(-11.7)^2}{16} = 8.56$$

$$SS(BC) = \frac{24.9^2}{16} = 38.75$$

$$SS(ABC) = \frac{23.9^2}{16} = 35.70$$

$$SSR = \frac{318.3^2 + 315.4^2}{8} = 25,098.48 = 0.53$$

$$SST = 34.6^2 + 46.4^2 + \ldots + 43.5^2 - 25,098.48$$
$$= 281.53$$

$$SSE = 281.53 - 62.02 - 64.40 - 0.01 - 18.28 - 8.56$$
$$- 38.75 - 35.70 - 0.53$$
$$= 53.28$$

(h) Analysis of variance table

Source of variation	Degrees of freedom	Sum of squares	Mean square
Replications	1	0.53	0.53
Main effects	3		
A	1	62.02	62.02
B	1	64.40	64.40
C	1	18.28	18.28
Two-factor interactions	3		
AB	1	0.01	0.01
AC	1	8.56	8.56
BC	1	38.75	38.75
Three-factor interactions	1		
ABC	1	35.70	35.70
Error	7	53.28	7.61
Total	15	281.53	

(i) The F statistics are

$$F_R = \frac{0.53}{7.61} = 0.07 \qquad F_A = \frac{62.02}{7.61} = 8.15$$

$$F_B = \frac{64.40}{7.61} = 8.46 \qquad F_C = \frac{18.28}{7.61} = 2.40$$

$$F_{AB} = \frac{0.01}{7.61} = 0.00 \qquad F_{AC} = \frac{8.56}{7.61} = 1.12$$

$$F_{BC} = \frac{38.75}{7.61} = 5.09 \qquad F_{ABC} = \frac{35.70}{7.61} = 4.69$$

Since $F_{.05} = 5.59$ for 1 and 7 degrees of freedom, it follows that the A and B main effects, but none of the others, is significant at a level of significance of 0.05. (At a level of significance of 0.01

none of the effects is significant since $F_{.01} = 12.25$ for 1 and 7 degrees of freedom.) The estimate of μ is

$$\hat{\mu} = \frac{633.7}{16} = 39.61$$

and the various effects are obtained by dividing the respective effect totals by 8. The estimated A and B main effects are thus

$$\frac{31.5}{8} = 3.94 \quad \text{and} \quad \frac{32.1}{8} = 4.01, \text{respectively.}$$

F.2a Confounding in a 2^3 factorial experiment (intrablock analysis)

Sometimes it is impossible to run all possible treatment combinations of a factorial arrangement in the same block. When the treatment combinations are, thus, divided among several blocks, some of the effects are confounded (inseparable) with block effects or with one another.

Suppose that in a 2^3 factorial experiment, where a complete block consists of 8 observations, it is possible to make only 4 observations at a time, that is, 4 observations per block. If treatment combinations a, b, c, and abc are contained in one block while treatment combinations 1, ab, ac, and bc in another, the "block effect," that is, the difference between the means obtained for the two blocks is

$$\tfrac{1}{4}[+(a) + (b) + (c) + (abc) - (1) - (ab) - (ac) - (bc)]$$

and it can be seen by inspection, from the table of signs on page 91, that this quantity is identical with the estimate of the ABC interaction. The ABC interaction is, thus, confounded with blocks, but all other factorial effects are measured within blocks, and are not confounded with blocks. Effect totals of confounded effects are sometimes called *interblock* comparisons, and those of unconfounded effects are called *intrablock* comparisons.

The following table shows all of the ways in which a single replication of a 2^3 factorial experiment may be confounded in two blocks:

Block 1				Block 2				Effect confounded with blocks
a	ab	ac	abc	1	bc	b	c	A
b	ab	bc	abc	1	a	c	ac	B
1	ab	c	abc	a	b	ac	bc	AB
c	ac	bc	abc	1	a	b	ab	C
1	b	ac	abc	a	c	ab	bc	AC
1	a	bc	abc	b	c	ab	ac	BC
a	b	c	abc	1	ab	ac	bc	ABC

DATA:

The data are like those of Section F.1 except that each replicate consists of two blocks. To illustrate the general procedure, the *ABC* interaction will be confounded; thus, treatment combinations *a*, *b*, *c*, and *abc* will be put into one block and treatment combinations 1, *ab*, *ac*, and *bc* in another in each replicate.

MODEL:

The model is like that of Section F.1 except that the *ABC* interaction must be considered to include block effects.

HYPOTHESES:

The hypotheses concerning the main effects and two-factor interactions remain unchanged; those concerning the confounded effect and replications are omitted.

CALCULATIONS:

The calculations for the analysis of variance of the intrablock (unconfounded) effects remain unchanged, with the exception that the sum of squares for replicates is not computed. Instead the following calculations are made:

(a′) Block sum of squares

$$SS(Bl) = \frac{\sum\limits_{m=1}^{2r} B_m^2}{2r} - C$$

where B_m is the total of the observations in the *m*th block.

(b′) Intrablock error sum of squares

$$SS(E_1) = SST - SSA - SSB - SSC - SS(AB) - SS(AC) \\ - SS(BC) - SS(Bl)$$

(c′) Intrablock analysis of variance table

Source of variation	Degrees of freedom	Sum of squares	Mean square
Blocks	$2r - 1$	SS(Bl)	
Main effects	3		
A	1	SSA	MSA = SSA
B	1	SSB	MSB = SSB
C	1	SSC	MSC = SSC
Two-factor interactions	3		
AB	1	SS(AB)	MS(AB) = SS(AB)
AC	1	SS(AC)	MS(AC) = SS(AC)
BC	1	SS(BC)	MS(BC) = SS(BC)
Error	$6(r - 1)$	SS(E$_1$)	$MS(E_1) = \dfrac{SS(E_1)}{6(r-1)}$
Total	$8r - 1$	SST	

(d') F statistics

The F statistics for main effects and two-factor interactions are obtained by dividing the appropriate mean squares by MS(E$_1$).

TESTS:

The null hypotheses concerning main effect and two-factor inter-actions are rejected at the level of significance α if the appropriate F ratios exceed F_α; they are accepted or judgment is reserved if they are less than or equal to F_α, where F_α is to be obtained from Table IV with 1 and $6(r - 1)$ degrees of freedom.

ESTIMATES:

The estimates of the unconfounded effects are like those of Section F.1.

EXAMPLE:

Suppose that in the ductility experiment of Section F.1 the alloys had to be melted in two different ovens because the capacity of neither oven was sufficient for all 8 specimens. Since the experiment was run in two replicates, there are now 4 oven charges, or blocks. The figures are unchanged and they may now be summarized as follows:

Treatment combination		Breaking strength (foot-pounds)	
		Rep. 1	Rep. 2
Blocks 1 & 3	a	46.4	42.4
	b	41.8	38.0
	c	37.8	32.7
	abc	46.2	43.5
Blocks 2 & 4	1	34.6	37.5
	ab	40.0	44.7
	ac	33.2	36.2
	bc	38.3	40.4

The four block totals are $B_1 = 172.2$, $B_2 = 146.1$, $B_3 = 156.6$, and $B_4 = 158.8$. The additional calculations required yield

(a') $\text{SS(Bl)} = \frac{1}{4}[172.2^2 + 146.1^2 + 156.6^2 + 158.8^2] - 25{,}098.48$
$= 86.28$

(b') $\text{SS(E}_1) = 281.53 - 62.02 - 64.40 - 18.28 - 0.01$
$\qquad\qquad\qquad\qquad\qquad\qquad -8.56 - 38.75 - 86.28$
$\qquad = 3.23$

using the values of SSA, SSB, . . . , obtained previously on page 96.

(c') Intrablock analysis of variance table

Source of variation	Degrees of freedom	Sum of squares	Mean square
Blocks	3	86.28	
Main effects	3		
A	1	62.02	62.02
B	1	64.40	64.40
C	1	18.28	18.28
Two-factor interactions	3		
AB	1	0.01	0.01
AC	1	8.56	8.56
BC	1	38.75	38.75
Error	6	3.23	0.54
Total	15	281.53	

(d') The F statistics are

$$F_A = \frac{62.02}{0.54} = 114.9 \qquad F_B = \frac{64.40}{0.54} = 119.3$$

$$F_C = \frac{18.28}{0.54} = 33.85 \qquad F_{AB} = \frac{0.01}{0.54} = 0.02$$

$$F_{AC} = \frac{8.56}{0.54} = 15.85 \qquad F_{BC} = \frac{38.75}{0.54} = 71.77$$

Since $F_{.05} = 5.99$ for 1 and 6 degrees of freedom, it follows that the A, B, and C main effects as well as the AC and BC interactions are significant at a level of significance of 0.05. (Since $F_{.01} = 13.75$ for 1 and 6 degrees of freedom, they are also significant at the level of significance of 0.01.)

F.2b Confounding in a 2^3 factorial experiment (interblock analysis)

Recovery of some of the confounded information on the *ABC* interaction is possible, but it requires replication and a new error term for *ABC*. The $2r - 1$ degrees of freedom for blocks may be broken down into $r - 1$ degrees of freedom for replicates, 1 degree of freedom for the *ABC* interaction, and $r - 1$ degrees of freedom for the interblock error.

CALCULATIONS:

SSR and SS(ABC) are calculated as in Section F.1, SS(Bl) as in Section F.2a, and

(a″) Interblock error sum of squares

$$SS(E_2) = SS(Bl) - SSR - SS(ABC)$$

(b″) Interblock analysis of variance table

Source of variation	Degrees of freedom	Sum of squares	Mean square
Replications	$r - 1$	SSR	$MSR = \dfrac{SSR}{r - 1}$
ABC	1	SS(ABC)	$MS(ABC) = SS(ABC)$
Interblock error	$r - 1$	$SS(E_2)$	$MS(E_2) = \dfrac{SS(E_2)}{r - 1}$
Total (blocks)	$2r - 1$	SS(Bl)	

(c″) *F* statistics

$$F_R = \frac{MSR}{MS(E_2)}$$

$$F_{ABC} = \frac{MS(ABC)}{MS(E_2)}$$

TESTS:

For replications the number of degrees of freedom for F_α are $r - 1$ and $r - 1$, for *ABC* they are 1 and $r - 1$.

Note: If confounding has been effective, the interblock error will be larger than the intrablock error, E_1. Furthermore the degrees of freedom for the interblock error are smaller. Thus, the test of significance for the confounded ABC interaction is made with far less precision than the other tests, that is, the tests of Section F.1a. Only when r, the number of replicates, is fairly large does it pay to make this test.

EXAMPLE:

Continuing the example of Section F.2a, it is already known from page 96 that SSR = 0.53, that SS(ABC) = 35.70, and from page 102 that SS(Bl) = 86.28. Thus

(a″) SS(E_2) = 86.28 − 0.53 − 35.70 = 50.05 and the inter-block analysis of variance table becomes

(b″)

Source of variation	Degrees of freedom	Sum of squares	Mean square
Replications	1	0.53	0.53
ABC	1	35.70	35.70
Interblock error	1	50.05	50.05
Total (blocks)	3	86.28	

(c″) The F statistics are

$$F_R = \frac{0.53}{50.05} = 0.01, \qquad F_{ABC} = \frac{35.70}{50.05} = 0.71$$

Since $F_{.05} = 161$ for 1 and 1 degrees of freedom, neither F_R nor F_{ABC} is significant.

F.2c Confounding in a 2^n factorial experiment

In principle, confounding in a 2^n factorial experiment is an extension of the work of the preceding sections; in practice, it is considerably more involved. It involves the concept of the generalized interaction of two effects, which is the "product" of these effects, with like letters canceled. Thus, the generalized interaction of AB and BC is $ABBC = AC$.

To confound a 2^n experiment in 2^p blocks of 2^{n-p} treatments within each replication, one confounds any p effects, provided that none is the generalized interaction of any of the others. Then a further $2^p - (p + 1)$ effects are automatically confounded, making $2^p - 1$ confounded effects in all. These are all the effects which can be expressed as generalized interactions of the group of effects originally selected for confounding. In practice, one ordinarily confounds only higher-order interactions and it should be noted, therefore, that if one chooses to confound $ABCD$ and BCD in a 2^4 factorial, the main effect A is also confounded.

When the effects to be confounded have been chosen, the assignment of treatment combinations to blocks must then be made. Each replicate is first divided into two blocks by confounding one effect, then into four by confounding another, etc. In practice, it may be desirable to refer to special tables constructed for this purpose.

The calculations are very similar to those of the preceding sections. Using appropriate tables of signs (like that on page 91) one calculates first the effect totals and, upon division by suitable divisors, obtains the required sums of squares.

F.3a Factorials at more than two levels

When the effects of some factors are known to be, or suspected to be, curvilinear over the range of experimentation, it is necessary to observe these factors at more than two levels. The number of levels at which a given factor is to be observed must be one more than the degree of the polynomial to be fitted to the response. This section and Section F.3b will serve to illustrate the analysis of a 4×3 factorial, that is, a factorial experiment in which one factor is observed at four levels and the other at three. The modification of this method of analysis to 3×2 factorials, 3×3 factorials, 5×4 factorials, etc., is immediate.

When there are two factors, A and B, the first at 4 levels and the second at 3, there are 12 observations in each complete block (replication), each observation representing a different combination of the levels of the factors, that is, a different treatment combination. With r replications there are, thus, $12r$ observations in the experiment. As in the 2^n series, the treatment combinations are represented by lower-case letters corresponding to the factors, but subscripts are used to indicate the level of each factor. Thus, a_1b_1 stands for the treatment combination in which factors A and B are both at level 1, a_4b_2 stands for the treatment combination in which factor A is at the fourth level and factor B at the second, a_3b_1 stands for the treatment combination in which factor A is at the third level and factor B at the first, etc.

The material of this section consists, essentially, of a two-way analysis of variance with replication like that of Section E.5. In Section F.3b it will be shown how the sums of squares can be broken down further to investigate the nature of the effects, namely, to investigate whether they are linear, quadratic, etc.

DATA:

Treatment combination	Level of factor A	B	First replicate		rth replicate
a_1b_1	1	1	x_{111}	. .	x_{11r}
a_1b_2	1	2	x_{121}	. .	x_{12r}
a_1b_3	1	3	x_{131}	. .	x_{13r}
a_2b_1	2	1	x_{211}	. .	x_{21r}
a_2b_2	2	2	x_{221}	. .	x_{22r}
a_2b_3	2	3	x_{231}	. .	x_{23r}
a_3b_1	3	1	x_{311}	. .	x_{31r}
a_3b_2	3	2	x_{321}	. .	x_{32r}
a_3b_3	3	3	x_{331}	. .	x_{33r}
a_4b_1	4	1	x_{411}	. .	x_{41r}
a_4b_2	4	2	x_{421}	. .	x_{42r}
a_4b_3	4	3	x_{431}	. .	x_{43r}

Here x_{ijk} is the observation taken at the ith level of A, the jth level of B, in the kth replicate. The subscript i assumes the values 1, 2, 3, 4, the subscript j assumes the values 1, 2, 3, and the subscript k assumes the values 1, 2, . . . , r. The sum of all observations receiving a particular treatment combination will be symbolized by enclosing the corresponding letters in parentheses. Thus, (a_2b_3) denotes the sum of all observations which receive the treatment combination a_2b_3; (a_4b_1) denotes the sum of all observations which receive the treatment combination a_4b_1, etc. Also (A_i), with $i = 1, 2, 3,$ or 4 stands for the sum of all observations at the ith level of A, regardless of the level of the other factor, and (B_j), with $j = 1, 2,$ or 3 stands for the sum of all observations at the jth level of B; T_k stands for the total of the kth replication, and T for the grand total of all observations.

MODEL:

$$x_{ijk} = \mu + \alpha_i + \beta_j + \rho_k + (\alpha\beta)_{ij} + \epsilon_{ijk} \quad \begin{cases} i = 1, 2, 3, 4 \\ j = 1, 2, 3 \\ k = 1, 2, \ldots, r \end{cases}$$

where μ is the over-all mean, α_i is the effect of the ith level of factor A, β_j is the effect of the jth level of factor B, ρ_k is the effect of the kth replicate, and $(\alpha\beta)_{ij}$ is the interaction of the ith level of A with the jth level of B. These parameters are subject to the restriction that the sums of the α_i, the β_j, and the ρ_k are equal to 0, respectively, and that the sums of the $(\alpha\beta)_{ij}$ are equal to 0 when summed on either i or j. The ϵ_{ijk} are independent chance components with identical normal distributions $N(0, \sigma)$.

HYPOTHESES:

For factor A:
Null hypothesis: $\alpha_i = 0$ for all i
Alternative hypothesis: the α_i are not all equal to 0.
For factor B:
Null hypothesis: $\beta_j = 0$ for all j
Alternative hypothesis: the β_j are not all equal to 0.
For replications:
Null hypothesis: $\rho_k = 0$ for all k
Alternative hypothesis: the ρ_k are not all equal to 0.
For AB interaction:
Null hypothesis: $(\alpha\beta)_{ij} = 0$ for all i and j
Alternative hypothesis: the $(\alpha\beta)_{ij}$ are not all equal to 0.

CALCULATIONS:

(a) Correction term
$$C = \frac{T^2}{12r}$$

(b) Factor A sum of squares
$$\text{SSA} = \frac{\sum\limits_{i=1}^{4} (A_i)^2}{3r} - C$$

(c) Factor B sum of squares
$$\text{SSB} = \frac{\sum\limits_{i=1}^{3} (B_j)^2}{4r} - C$$

(d) AB interaction sum of squares
$$\text{SS(AB)} = \frac{\sum\limits_{i=1}^{4} \sum\limits_{j=1}^{3} (a_i b_j)^2}{r} - C - \text{SSA} - \text{SSB}$$

(e) Replication sum of squares

$$\text{SSR} = \frac{\sum\limits_{k=1}^{r} T_k^2}{12} - C$$

(f) Total sum of squares

$$\text{SST} = \sum_{i=1}^{4} \sum_{j=1}^{3} \sum_{k=1}^{r} x_{ijk}^2 - C$$

(g) Error sum of squares

$$\text{SSE} = \text{SST} - \text{SSA} - \text{SSB} - \text{SS(AB)} - \text{SSR}$$

(h) Analysis of variance table

Source of variation	Degrees of freedom	Sum of squares	Mean square
Replication	$r - 1$	SSR	$\text{MSR} = \dfrac{\text{SSR}}{r-1}$
Factor A	3	SSA	$\text{MSA} = \dfrac{\text{SSA}}{3}$
Factor B	2	SSB	$\text{MSB} = \dfrac{\text{SSB}}{2}$
Interaction AB	6	SS(AB)	$\text{MS(AB)} = \dfrac{\text{SS(AB)}}{6}$
Error	$11(r-1)$	SSE	$\text{MSE} = \dfrac{\text{SSE}}{11(r-1)}$
Total	$12r - 1$	SST	

(i) F statistics

$$F_A = \frac{\text{MSA}}{\text{MSE}} \qquad F_B = \frac{\text{MSB}}{\text{MSE}}$$

$$F_R = \frac{\text{MSR}}{\text{MSE}} \qquad F_{AB} = \frac{\text{MS(AB)}}{\text{MSE}}$$

TESTS:

Reject the null hypothesis at the level of significance α if the appropriate F ratio exceeds F_α; accept the null hypothesis or reserve judgment if it is less than or equal to F_α, where F_α is to be obtained from Table IV. The number of degrees of freedom are 3 and $11(r-1)$ for Factor A, 2 and $11(r-1)$ for Factor B, $r-1$ and $11(r-1)$ for replications, and 6 and $11(r-1)$ for the AB interaction.

EXAMPLE:

Two groups of 12 laboratory rats were deprived of food, except for one hour per day, for several weeks. At the end of that time each rat was inoculated with a given dose of a certain drug and, after a specified amount of time, was fed. The weight (in grams) of the food ingested by each rat was measured. The purpose of the experiment is to determine the effect of the drug on the motivation of the rats. In the table given below, the first entry in each cell is the grams of food ingested by a rat in the first group, and the second entry is that for a rat of the second group:

B Time before feeding (hours)	A, Dosage (mg/kg)			
	0.1	0.3	0.5	0.7
1	9.07 8.77	5.63 8.76	4.42 3.01	1.38 3.96
5	9.16 11.82	11.57 11.53	5.22 9.21	5.72 4.69
9	16.08 14.65	10.37 14.46	7.27 6.10	5.48 9.28

The required totals are

$$(a_1b_1) = 17.84, \quad (a_2b_1) = 14.39, \quad (a_3b_1) = 7.43,$$
$$(a_4b_1) = 5.34, \quad (a_1b_2) = 20.98, \quad (a_2b_2) = 23.10,$$
$$(a_3b_2) = 14.43, \quad (a_4b_2) = 10.41, \quad (a_1b_3) = 30.73,$$
$$(a_2b_3) = 24.83, \quad (a_3b_3) = 13.37, \quad (a_4b_3) = 14.76,$$
$$(A_1) = 69.55, \quad (A_2) = 62.32, \quad (A_3) = 35.23,$$
$$(A_4) = 30.51, \quad (B_1) = 45.00, \quad (B_2) = 68.92,$$
$$(B_3) = 83.69, \quad T_1 = 91.37, \quad T_2 = 106.24,$$
$$T = 197.61,$$

and the calculations yield

(a) $\quad C = \dfrac{197.61^2}{24} = 1{,}627.0713$

(b) $\quad \text{SSA} = \dfrac{69.55^2 + 62.32^2 + 35.23^2 + 30.51^2}{6} - 1627.0713$

$\qquad\qquad = 188.4284$

(c) $\quad \text{SSB} = \dfrac{45.00^2 + 68.92^2 + 83.69^2}{8} - 1{,}627.0713$

$\qquad\qquad = 95.3015$

(d) $\text{SS(AB)} = \dfrac{17.84^2 + 14.39^2 + \ldots + 14.76^2}{2} - 1{,}627.0713$

$\qquad\qquad\qquad\qquad\qquad\qquad - 188.4284 - 95.3015$

$\qquad\qquad = 17.6487$

(e) $\quad \text{SSR} = \dfrac{91.37^2 + 106.24^2}{12} - 1{,}627.0713 = 9.2132$

(f) $\quad \text{SST} = 9.07^2 + 8.77^2 + \ldots + 9.28^2 - 1{,}627.0713$

$\qquad\qquad = 339.9634$

(g) $\quad \text{SSE} = 339.9634 - 188.4284 - 95.3015 - 17.6478$

$\qquad\qquad\qquad\qquad\qquad\qquad\qquad\qquad - 9.2132$

$\qquad\qquad = 29.3725$

and the analysis of variance table becomes

Source of variation	Degrees of freedom	Sum of squares	Mean square
Replication	1	9.2132	9.2132
Factor A	3	188.4284	62.8095
Factor B	2	95.3015	47.6508
Interaction AB	6	17.6478	2.9413
Error	11	29.3725	2.6702
Total	23	339.9634	

The F ratios are

$$F_R = \frac{9.2132}{2.6702} = 3.45 \qquad F_A = \frac{62.8095}{2.6702} = 23.52$$

$$F_B = \frac{47.6508}{2.6702} = 17.85 \qquad F_{AB} = \frac{2.9413}{2.6702} = 1.10$$

and since $F_{.05} = 4.84$ for 1 and 11 degrees of freedom, $F_{.05} = 3.98$ for 2 and 11 degrees of freedom, $F_{.05} = 3.59$ for 3 and 11 degrees of freedom, and $F_{.05} = 3.09$ for 6 and 11 degrees of freedom, the effects of factors A and B are significant at the level of significance of 0.05, while those of replication and the AB interaction are not.

F.3b Single degree of freedom comparisons

There are many problems in which it is not only important to test the significance of main effects and interactions, but where it is also of interest to see how the variable under consideration (weight of food ingested in the example of the preceding section) is affected by the various levels of a factor. In other words, it is of interest also to see what kind of mathematical curve, usually a polynomial, can be fitted to the values obtained for various levels of a factor. Of course, such an analysis is called for only when the levels of a factor are *numerical*, not when they are qualitative, such as severe cracks, minor cracks, no cracks, etc.

If a factor is measured at p levels, it is possible to fit a polynomial of degree $p - 1$, that is, one can test hypotheses concerning a linear effect, quadratic effect, cubic effect, . . . , and an effect of degree $p - 1$. These tests are based on orthogonal comparisons obtained in a manner similar to the effect totals on page 91, only the coefficients can be numbers other than $+1$ and -1. When the levels of a factor are equally spaced, these coefficients may be obtained from a table of orthogonal polynomials; when they are not equally spaced, polynomial coefficients may be generated, but the procedure is beyond the scope of this manual. The following are the coefficients used for factors measured at 2, 3, and 4 levels:

Two levels: Linear effect: -1 $+1$

Three levels: Linear effect: -1 0 1
                  Quadratic effect: 1 -2 1

Four levels: Linear effect: -3 -1 1 3
                  Quadratic effect: 1 -1 -1 1
                  Cubic effect: -1 3 -3 1

Like the $+1$'s and -1's on page 91, these coefficients are multiplied by the totals for the successive levels of a factor and their sum gives the desired comparison. Thus, if a factor A is measured at four levels, the linear effect comparison is

$$-3(A_1) - (A_2) + (A_3) + 3(A_4)$$

the quadratic effect comparison is

$$(A_1) - (A_2) - (A_3) + (A_4)$$

and the cubic effect comparison is

$$-(A_1) + 3(A_2) - 3(A_3) + (A_4)$$

To divide the sum of squares of a factor into single degree of freedom components attributed to its linear effect, quadratic effect, etc., one has only to divide the *squares* of the respective comparisons by suitable divisors. The divisor is obtained in each case by multiplying the sum of the squares of the coefficients by the number of observations made at each level of the factor. Thus, if there are n observations made at each of the four levels of a factor A, the sum of squares due to the linear effect is

$$\mathrm{SS}(A_L) = \frac{[-3(A_1) - (A_2) + (A_3) + 3(A_4)]^2}{20n}$$

and it has 1 degree of freedom.

Sums of squares due to interactions may also be broken down into single degree of freedom components attributed, say, to the interaction between the linear effect of A and the quadratic effect of B, the cubic effect of A and the linear effect of B, . . . , but the necessary formulas and methods will not be given in this manual.

EXAMPLE:

Referring to the data of Section F.3a and analyzing first factor A, the linear, quadratic, and cubic comparisons are, respectively,

$$-3(69.5) - 62.32 + 35.23 + 3(30.51) = -144.21$$
$$69.5 - 62.32 - 35.32 + 30.51 = 2.51$$
$$-69.5 + 3(62.32) - 3(35.23) - 30.51 = 42.23$$

and the sums of squares are

$$\mathrm{SS}(A_L) = \frac{(-144.21)^2}{120} = 173.3044$$

$$\mathrm{SS}(A_Q) = \frac{(2.51)^2}{24} = 0.2625$$

$$\mathrm{SS}(A_C) = \frac{(42.23)^2}{120} = 14.8614$$

Using the error term from page 113, namely, MSE = 2.6702 with 11 degrees of freedom, the F ratios for the linear, quadratic, and cubic effects of factor A become

$$F_{A_L} = \frac{173.3044}{2.6702} = 64.90$$

$$F_{A_Q} = \frac{0.2625}{2.6702} = 0.10$$

$$F_{A_c} = \frac{14.8614}{2.6702} = 5.56$$

Since $F_{.05} = 4.84$ for 1 and 11 degrees of freedom, it follows that the linear and cubic components of factor A are significant at the 0.05 level of significance, while the quadratic component is not. (Analyzing factor B in the same fashion, it can be shown that the linear effect is significant at the 0.05 or 0.01 levels of significance, while the quadratic effect is not.)

Bibliography

The following books deal primarily with problems of experimental statistics.

Anderson, R. L., and Bancroft, T. A., *Statistical Theory in Research*. New York: McGraw-Hill, 1952.

Bennett, C. A., and Franklin, N. L., *Statistical Analysis in Chemistry and the Chemical Industry*. New York: Wiley, 1954.

Bowker, A. H., and Lieberman, G. J., *Handbook of Industrial Statistics*. Englewood Cliffs, N. J.: Prentice-Hall, 1955.

Brownlee, K. A., *Industrial Experimentation*. Brooklyn: Chemical Publishing Co., 1949.

Chew, V., *Experimental Designs in Industry*. New York: Wiley, 1958.

Cochran, W. G., and Cox, G. M., *Experimental Designs*, 2nd ed. New York: Wiley, 1957.

Cox, D. R., *Planning of Experiments*. New York: Wiley, 1958.

Davies, O. L., *The Design and Analysis of Industrial Experiments*. New York: Hafner, 1956.

Edwards, A. L., *Experimental Design in Psychological Research*. New York: Rinehart, 1950.

Federer, W. T., *Experimental Design, Theory and Application*. New York: Macmillan, 1955.

Finney, D. J., *Experimental Design and Its Statistical Basis*. Chicago: University of Chicago Press, 1955.

Fisher, R. A., *Statistical Methods for Research Workers*, 10th ed. New York: Hafner, 1948.

Fisher, R. A., *The Design of Experiments*, 4th ed. New York: Hafner, 1947.

Hald, A., *Statistical Theory with Engineering Applications*. New York: Wiley, 1952.

Kempthorne, O., *The Design and Analysis of Experiments*. New York: Wiley, 1952.

Lindquist, E. F., *Design and Analysis of Experiments in Psychology and Education*. Boston: Houghton Mifflin, 1953.

Mann, H. B., *Analysis and Design of Experiments*. New York: Dover, 1949.

Ostle, B., *Statistics in Research*. Ames, Iowa: Iowa State College Press, 1954.

Quenouille, M. H., *The Design and Analysis of Experiments*. London: Charles Griffin & Co., 1953.

Yates, F., *The Design and Analysis of Factorial Experiments*. Harpenden, England: Imperial Bureau of Soil Science, 1937.

The following are tables that are widely used in experimental statistics.

Fisher, R. A., and Yates, F., *Statistical Tables for Biological, Agricultural, and Medical Research*, 3d ed. New York: Hafner, 1949.

Kitagawa, T., and Mitome, M., *Tables for the Design of Factorial Experiments*. New York: Dover, 1953.

Pearson, E. S., and Hartley, H. O., *Biometrika Tables for Statisticians*, Vol I. Cambridge: Cambridge University Press, 1954.

Those who are not too well versed in the language of statistics will find it useful to refer to:

Kendall, M. G., and Buckland, W. R., *A Dictionary of Statistical Terms*. Edinburgh: Oliver and Boyd, 1957.

Statistical Tables

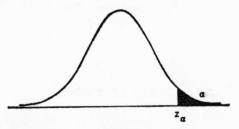

Figure 1

Table I contains areas under the standard normal distribution, that is, the normal distribution whose mean and standard deviation are $\mu = 0$ and $\sigma = 1$. For any given value of z, the entry of Table I is the area under the standard normal distribution to the right of z, namely, the probability of exceeding the particular value of z. Thus, the probability of exceeding $z = 0.48$ is 0.3156, the probability of exceeding $z = 2.15$ is 0.0158, and $z_{.025} = 1.96$. As is illustrated in Figure 1, z_α is the value of z which is such that the area under the standard normal distribution to its right equals α. In view of the symmetry of the normal distribution, the area under the curve to the left of $-z$ equals that to the right of z. *Note:* The normal distribution having the mean μ and the standard deviation σ is referred to by the symbol $N(\mu, \sigma)$. Thus, for example, $N(0, 1)$ stands for the standard normal distribution.

Table I. Normal Curve Areas*

z	.00	.01	.02	.03	.04	.05	.06	.07	.08	.09
0.0	.5000	.4960	.4920	.4880	.4840	.4801	.4761	.4721	.4681	.4641
0.1	.4602	.4562	.4522	.4483	.4443	.4404	.4364	.4325	.4286	.4247
0.2	.4207	.4168	.4129	.4090	.4052	.4013	.3974	.3936	.3897	.3859
0.3	.3821	.3783	.3745	.3707	.3669	.3632	.3594	.3557	.3520	.3483
0.4	.3446	.3409	.3372	.3336	.3300	.3264	.3228	.3192	.3156	.3121
0.5	.3085	.3050	.3015	.2981	.2946	.2912	.2877	.2843	.2810	.2776
0.6	.2743	.2709	.2676	.2643	.2611	.2578	.2546	.2514	.2483	.2451
0.7	.2420	.2389	.2358	.2327	.2296	.2266	.2236	.2206	.2177	.2148
0.8	.2119	.2090	.2061	.2033	.2005	.1977	.1949	.1922	.1894	.1867
0.9	.1841	.1814	.1788	.1762	.1736	.1711	.1685	.1660	.1635	.1611
1.0	.1587	.1562	.1539	.1515	.1492	.1469	.1446	.1423	.1401	.1379
1.1	.1357	.1335	.1314	.1292	.1271	.1251	.1230	.1210	.1190	.1170
1.2	.1151	.1131	.1112	.1093	.1075	.1056	.1038	.1020	.1003	.0985
1.3	.0968	.0951	.0934	.0918	.0901	.0885	.0869	.0853	.0838	.0823
1.4	.0808	.0793	.0778	.0764	.0749	.0735	.0721	.0708	.0694	.0681
1.5	.0668	.0655	.0643	.0630	.0618	.0606	.0594	.0582	.0571	.0559
1.6	.0548	.0537	.0526	.0516	.0505	.0495	.0485	.0475	.0465	.0455
1.7	.0446	.0436	.0427	.0418	.0409	.0401	.0392	.0384	.0375	.0367
1.8	.0359	.0351	.0344	.0336	.0329	.0322	.0314	.0307	.0301	.0294
1.9	.0287	.0281	.0274	.0268	.0262	.0256	.0250	.0244	.0239	.0233
2.0	.0228	.0222	.0217	.0212	.0207	.0202	.0197	.0192	.0188	.0183
2.1	.0179	.0174	.0170	.0166	.0162	.0158	.0154	.0150	.0146	.0143
2.2	.0139	.0136	.0132	.0129	.0125	.0122	.0119	.0116	.0113	.0110
2.3	.0107	.0104	.0102	.00990	.00964	.00939	.00914	.00889	.00866	.00842
2.4	.00820	.00798	.00776	.00755	.00734	.00714	.00695	.00676	.00657	.00639
2.5	.00621	.00604	.00587	.00570	.00554	.00539	.00523	.00508	.00494	.00480
2.6	.00466	.00453	.00440	.00427	.00415	.00402	.00391	.00379	.00368	.00357
2.7	.00347	.00336	.00326	.00317	.00307	.00298	.00289	.00280	.00272	.00264
2.8	.00256	.00248	.00240	.00233	.00226	.00219	.00212	.00205	.00199	.00193
2.9	.00187	.00181	.00175	.00169	.00164	.00159	.00154	.00149	.00144	.00139

* Reprinted by permission from Frederick E. Croxton, *Elementary Statistics with Applications in Medicine.* Englewood Cliffs, N. J.: Prentice-Hall, Inc., 1953, p. 323.

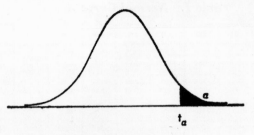

Figure 2

Table II contains the values of $t_{.10}$, $t_{.05}$, $t_{.025}$, $t_{.01}$, and $t_{.005}$ for d.f. (the number of degrees of freedom) going from 1 to 29. Here $t_{.025}$ stands for the value of t which is exceeded by 2.5 per cent of the area under the Student-t distribution, $t_{.01}$ for the value of t which is exceeded by 1 per cent of the area under the Student-t distribution, etc. In view of the symmetry of the Student-t distribution, the area under the curve to the left of $-t$ equals that to the right of t.

Table II. Values of t^*

d.f.	$t_{.100}$	$t_{.050}$	$t_{.025}$	$t_{.010}$	$t_{.005}$	d.f.
1	3.078	6.314	12.706	31.821	63.657	1
2	1.886	2.920	4.303	6.965	9.925	2
3	1.638	2.353	3.182	4.541	5.841	3
4	1.533	2.132	2.776	3.747	4.604	4
5	1.476	2.015	2.571	3.365	4.032	5
6	1.440	1.943	2.447	3.143	3.707	6
7	1.415	1.895	2.365	2.998	3.499	7
8	1.397	1.860	2.306	2.896	3.355	8
9	1.383	1.833	2.262	2.821	3.250	9
10	1.372	1.812	2.228	2.764	3.169	10
11	1.363	1.796	2.201	2.718	3.106	11
12	1.356	1.782	2.179	2.681	3.055	12
13	1.350	1.771	2.160	2.650	3.012	13
14	1.345	1.761	2.145	2.624	2.977	14
15	1.341	1.753	2.131	2.602	2.947	15
16	1.337	1.746	2.120	2.583	2.921	16
17	1.333	1.740	2.110	2.567	2.898	17
18	1.330	1.734	2.101	2.552	2.878	18
19	1.328	1.729	2.093	2.539	2.861	19
20	1.325	1.725	2.086	2.528	2.845	20
21	1.323	1.721	2.080	2.518	2.831	21
22	1.321	1.717	2.074	2.508	2.819	22
23	1.319	1.714	2.069	2.500	2.807	23
24	1.318	1.711	2.064	2.492	2.797	24
25	1.316	1.708	2.060	2.485	2.787	25
26	1.315	1.706	2.056	2.479	2.779	26
27	1.314	1.703	2.052	2.473	2.771	27
28	1.313	1.701	2.048	2.467	2.763	28
29	1.311	1.699	2.045	2.462	2.756	29
inf.	1.282	1.645	1.960	2.326	2.576	inf.

* This table is abridged from Table IV of R. A. Fisher, *Statistical Methods for Research Workers*, published by Oliver and Boyd, Ltd., Edinburgh, by permission of the author and publishers.

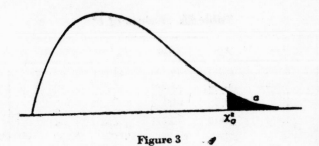

Figure 3

Table III contains the values of $\chi^2_{.99}$, $\chi^2_{.98}$, $\chi^2_{.95}$, $\chi^2_{.05}$, $\chi^2_{.02}$, and $\chi^2_{.01}$ for *d.f.* (the number of degrees of freedom) going from 1 to 30. Here $\chi^2_{.98}$ stands for the value of χ^2 which is exceeded by 98 per cent of the area under the χ^2 distribution, $\chi^2_{.02}$ for the value of χ^2 which is exceeded by 2 per cent of the area under the χ^2 distribution, etc.

Table III. Values of χ^2*

d.f.	$\chi^2_{.99}$	$\chi^2_{.98}$	$\chi^2_{.95}$	$\chi^2_{.05}$	$\chi^2_{.02}$	$\chi^2_{.01}$	d.f.
1	.000157	.000628	.00393	3.841	5.412	6.635	1
2	.0201	.0404	.103	5.991	7.824	9.210	2
3	.115	.185	.352	7.815	9.837	11.341	3
4	.297	.429	.711	9.488	11.668	13.277	4
5	.554	.752	1.145	11.070	13.388	15.086	5
6	.872	1.134	1.635	12.592	15.033	16.812	6
7	1.239	1.564	2.167	14.067	16.622	18.475	7
8	1.646	2.032	2.733	15.507	18.168	20.090	8
9	2.088	2.532	3.325	16.919	19.679	21.666	9
10	2.558	3.059	3.940	18.307	21.161	23.209	10
11	3.053	3.609	4.575	19.675	22.618	24.725	11
12	3.571	4.178	5.226	21.026	24.054	26.217	12
13	4.107	4.765	5.892	22.362	25.472	27.688	13
14	4.660	5.368	6.571	23.685	26.873	29.141	14
15	5.229	5.985	7.261	24.996	28.259	30.578	15
16	5.812	6.614	7.962	26.296	29.633	32.000	16
17	6.408	7.255	8.672	27.587	30.995	33.409	17
18	7.015	7.906	9.390	28.869	32.346	34.805	18
19	7.633	8.567	10.117	30.144	33.687	36.191	19
20	8.260	9.237	10.851	31.410	35.020	37.566	20
21	8.897	9.915	11.591	32.671	36.343	38.932	21
22	9.542	10.600	12.338	33.924	37.659	40.289	22
23	10.196	11.293	13.091	35.172	38.968	41.638	23
24	10.856	11.992	13.848	36.415	40.270	42.980	24
25	11.524	12.697	14.611	37.652	41.566	44.314	25
26	12.198	13.409	15.379	38.885	42.856	45.642	26
27	12.879	14.125	16.151	40.113	44.140	46.963	27
28	13.565	14.847	16.928	41.337	45.419	48.278	28
29	14.256	15.574	17.708	42.557	46.693	49.588	29
30	14.953	16.306	18.493	43.773	47.962	50.892	30

* This table is abridged from Table III of R. A. Fisher, *Statistical Methods for Research Workers*, published by Oliver and Boyd, Ltd., Edinburgh, by permission of the author and publishers.

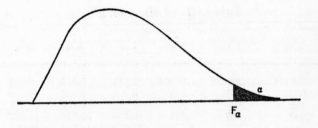

Figure 4

Tables IVa and IVb contain values of $F_{.05}$ and $F_{.01}$, respectively. Here $F_{.05}$ stands for the value of F which is exceeded by 5 per cent of the area under the F distribution, and $F_{.01}$ for the value of F which is exceeded by 1 per cent of the area under the F distribution. Throughout this manual the degrees of freedom for the numerator are listed first and those for the denominator second. Thus, for 2 and 20 degrees of freedom $F_{.05} = 3.49$, and for 5 and 9 degrees of freedom $F_{.01} = 6.06$.

Table IVa. Values of $F_{.05}$*

Degrees of freedom for numerator

	1	2	3	4	5	6	7	8	9	10	12	15	20	24	30	40	60	120	∞
1	161	200	216	225	230	234	237	239	241	242	244	246	248	249	250	251	252	253	254
2	18.5	19.0	19.2	19.2	19.3	19.3	19.4	19.4	19.4	19.4	19.4	19.4	19.4	19.5	19.5	19.5	19.5	19.5	19.5
3	10.1	9.55	9.28	9.12	9.01	8.94	8.89	8.85	8.81	8.79	8.74	8.70	8.66	8.64	8.62	8.59	8.57	8.55	8.53
4	7.71	6.94	6.59	6.39	6.26	6.16	6.09	6.04	6.00	5.96	5.91	5.86	5.80	5.77	5.75	5.72	5.69	5.66	5.63
5	6.61	5.79	5.41	5.19	5.05	4.95	4.88	4.82	4.77	4.74	4.68	4.62	4.56	4.53	4.50	4.46	4.43	4.40	4.37
6	5.99	5.14	4.76	4.53	4.39	4.28	4.21	4.15	4.10	4.06	4.00	3.94	3.87	3.84	3.81	3.77	3.74	3.70	3.67
7	5.59	4.74	4.35	4.12	3.97	3.87	3.79	3.73	3.68	3.64	3.57	3.51	3.44	3.41	3.38	3.34	3.30	3.27	3.23
8	5.32	4.46	4.07	3.84	3.69	3.58	3.50	3.44	3.39	3.35	3.28	3.22	3.15	3.12	3.08	3.04	3.01	2.97	2.93
9	5.12	4.26	3.86	3.63	3.48	3.37	3.29	3.23	3.18	3.14	3.07	3.01	2.94	2.90	2.86	2.83	2.79	2.75	2.71
10	4.96	4.10	3.71	3.48	3.33	3.22	3.14	3.07	3.02	2.98	2.91	2.85	2.77	2.74	2.70	2.66	2.62	2.58	2.54
11	4.84	3.98	3.59	3.36	3.20	3.09	3.01	2.95	2.90	2.85	2.79	2.72	2.65	2.61	2.57	2.53	2.49	2.45	2.40
12	4.75	3.89	3.49	3.26	3.11	3.00	2.91	2.85	2.80	2.75	2.69	2.62	2.54	2.51	2.47	2.43	2.38	2.34	2.30
13	4.67	3.81	3.41	3.18	3.03	2.92	2.83	2.77	2.71	2.67	2.60	2.53	2.46	2.42	2.38	2.34	2.30	2.25	2.21
14	4.60	3.74	3.34	3.11	2.96	2.85	2.76	2.70	2.65	2.60	2.53	2.46	2.39	2.35	2.31	2.27	2.22	2.18	2.13
15	4.54	3.68	3.29	3.06	2.90	2.79	2.71	2.64	2.59	2.54	2.48	2.40	2.33	2.29	2.25	2.20	2.16	2.11	2.07
16	4.49	3.63	3.24	3.01	2.85	2.74	2.66	2.59	2.54	2.49	2.42	2.35	2.28	2.24	2.19	2.15	2.11	2.06	2.01
17	4.45	3.59	3.20	2.96	2.81	2.70	2.61	2.55	2.49	2.45	2.38	2.31	2.23	2.19	2.15	2.10	2.06	2.01	1.96
18	4.41	3.55	3.16	2.93	2.77	2.66	2.58	2.51	2.46	2.41	2.34	2.27	2.19	2.15	2.11	2.06	2.02	1.97	1.92
19	4.38	3.52	3.13	2.90	2.74	2.63	2.54	2.48	2.42	2.38	2.31	2.23	2.16	2.11	2.07	2.03	1.98	1.93	1.88
20	4.35	3.49	3.10	2.87	2.71	2.60	2.51	2.45	2.39	2.35	2.28	2.20	2.12	2.08	2.04	1.99	1.95	1.90	1.84
21	4.32	3.47	3.07	2.84	2.68	2.57	2.49	2.42	2.37	2.32	2.25	2.18	2.10	2.05	2.01	1.96	1.92	1.87	1.81
22	4.30	3.44	3.05	2.82	2.66	2.55	2.46	2.40	2.34	2.30	2.23	2.15	2.07	2.03	1.98	1.94	1.89	1.84	1.78
23	4.28	3.42	3.03	2.80	2.64	2.53	2.44	2.37	2.32	2.27	2.20	2.13	2.05	2.01	1.96	1.91	1.86	1.81	1.76
24	4.26	3.40	3.01	2.78	2.62	2.51	2.42	2.36	2.30	2.25	2.18	2.11	2.03	1.98	1.94	1.89	1.84	1.79	1.73
25	4.24	3.39	2.99	2.76	2.60	2.49	2.40	2.34	2.28	2.24	2.16	2.09	2.01	1.96	1.92	1.87	1.82	1.77	1.71
30	4.17	3.32	2.92	2.69	2.53	2.42	2.33	2.27	2.21	2.16	2.09	2.01	1.93	1.89	1.84	1.79	1.74	1.68	1.62
40	4.08	3.23	2.84	2.61	2.45	2.34	2.25	2.18	2.12	2.08	2.00	1.92	1.84	1.79	1.74	1.69	1.64	1.58	1.51
60	4.00	3.15	2.76	2.53	2.37	2.25	2.17	2.10	2.04	1.99	1.92	1.84	1.75	1.70	1.65	1.59	1.53	1.47	1.39
120	3.92	3.07	2.68	2.45	2.29	2.18	2.09	2.02	1.96	1.91	1.83	1.75	1.66	1.61	1.55	1.50	1.43	1.35	1.25
∞	3.84	3.00	2.60	2.37	2.21	2.10	2.01	1.94	1.88	1.83	1.75	1.67	1.57	1.52	1.46	1.39	1.32	1.22	1.00

Degrees of freedom for denominator

127

* This table is reproduced from M. Merrington and C. M. Thompson, "Tables of percentage points of the inverted beta (F) distribution," *Biometrika*, Vol. 33 (1943), by permission of the *Biometrika* trustees.

Table IVb. Values of $F_{.01}$*

Degrees of freedom for numerator

	1	2	3	4	5	6	7	8	9	10	12	15	20	24	30	40	60	120	∞
1	4,052	5,000	5,403	5,625	5,764	5,859	5,928	5,982	6,023	6,056	6,106	6,157	6,209	6,235	6,261	6,287	6,313	6,339	6,366
2	98.5	99.0	99.2	99.2	99.3	99.3	99.4	99.4	99.4	99.4	99.4	99.4	99.4	99.5	99.5	99.5	99.5	99.5	99.5
3	34.1	30.8	29.5	28.7	28.2	27.9	27.7	27.5	27.3	27.2	27.1	26.9	26.7	26.6	26.5	26.4	26.3	26.2	26.1
4	21.2	18.0	16.7	16.0	15.5	15.2	15.0	14.8	14.7	14.5	14.4	14.2	14.0	13.9	13.8	13.7	13.7	13.6	13.5
5	16.3	13.3	12.1	11.4	11.0	10.7	10.5	10.3	10.2	10.1	9.89	9.72	9.55	9.47	9.38	9.29	9.20	9.11	9.02
6	13.7	10.9	9.78	9.15	8.75	8.47	8.26	8.10	7.98	7.87	7.72	7.56	7.40	7.31	7.23	7.14	7.06	6.97	6.88
7	12.2	9.55	8.45	7.85	7.46	7.19	6.99	6.84	6.72	6.62	6.47	6.31	6.16	6.07	5.99	5.91	5.82	5.74	5.65
8	11.3	8.65	7.59	7.01	6.63	6.37	6.18	6.03	5.91	5.81	5.67	5.52	5.36	5.28	5.20	5.12	5.03	4.95	4.86
9	10.6	8.02	6.99	6.42	6.06	5.80	5.61	5.47	5.35	5.26	5.11	4.96	4.81	4.73	4.65	4.57	4.48	4.40	4.31
10	10.0	7.56	6.55	5.99	5.64	5.39	5.20	5.06	4.94	4.85	4.71	4.56	4.41	4.33	4.25	4.17	4.08	4.00	3.91
11	9.65	7.21	6.22	5.67	5.32	5.07	4.89	4.74	4.63	4.54	4.40	4.25	4.10	4.02	3.94	3.86	3.78	3.69	3.60
12	9.33	6.93	5.95	5.41	5.06	4.82	4.64	4.50	4.39	4.30	4.16	4.01	3.86	3.78	3.70	3.62	3.54	3.45	3.36
13	9.07	6.70	5.74	5.21	4.86	4.62	4.44	4.30	4.19	4.10	3.96	3.82	3.66	3.59	3.51	3.43	3.34	3.25	3.17
14	8.86	6.51	5.56	5.04	4.70	4.46	4.28	4.14	4.03	3.94	3.80	3.66	3.51	3.43	3.35	3.27	3.18	3.09	3.00
15	8.68	6.36	5.42	4.89	4.56	4.32	4.14	4.00	3.89	3.80	3.67	3.52	3.37	3.29	3.21	3.13	3.05	2.96	2.87
16	8.53	6.23	5.29	4.77	4.44	4.20	4.03	3.89	3.78	3.69	3.55	3.41	3.26	3.18	3.10	3.02	2.93	2.84	2.75
17	8.40	6.11	5.19	4.67	4.34	4.10	3.93	3.79	3.68	3.59	3.46	3.31	3.16	3.08	3.00	2.92	2.83	2.75	2.65
18	8.29	6.01	5.09	4.58	4.25	4.01	3.84	3.71	3.60	3.51	3.37	3.23	3.08	3.00	2.92	2.84	2.75	2.66	2.57
19	8.19	5.93	5.01	4.50	4.17	3.94	3.77	3.63	3.52	3.43	3.30	3.15	3.00	2.92	2.84	2.76	2.67	2.58	2.49
20	8.10	5.85	4.94	4.43	4.10	3.87	3.70	3.56	3.46	3.37	3.23	3.09	2.94	2.86	2.78	2.69	2.61	2.52	2.42
21	8.02	5.78	4.87	4.37	4.04	3.81	3.64	3.51	3.40	3.31	3.17	3.03	2.88	2.80	2.72	2.64	2.55	2.46	2.36
22	7.95	5.72	4.82	4.31	3.99	3.76	3.59	3.45	3.35	3.26	3.12	2.98	2.83	2.75	2.67	2.58	2.50	2.40	2.31
23	7.88	5.66	4.76	4.26	3.94	3.71	3.54	3.41	3.30	3.21	3.07	2.93	2.78	2.70	2.62	2.54	2.45	2.35	2.26
24	7.82	5.61	4.72	4.22	3.90	3.67	3.50	3.36	3.26	3.17	3.03	2.89	2.74	2.66	2.58	2.49	2.40	2.31	2.21
25	7.77	5.57	4.68	4.18	3.86	3.63	3.46	3.32	3.22	3.13	2.99	2.85	2.70	2.62	2.53	2.45	2.36	2.27	2.17
30	7.56	5.39	4.51	4.02	3.70	3.47	3.30	3.17	3.07	2.98	2.84	2.70	2.55	2.47	2.39	2.30	2.21	2.11	2.01
40	7.31	5.18	4.31	3.83	3.51	3.29	3.12	2.99	2.89	2.80	2.66	2.52	2.37	2.29	2.20	2.11	2.02	1.92	1.80
60	7.08	4.98	4.13	3.65	3.34	3.12	2.95	2.82	2.72	2.63	2.50	2.35	2.20	2.12	2.03	1.94	1.84	1.73	1.60
120	6.85	4.79	3.95	3.48	3.17	2.96	2.79	2.66	2.56	2.47	2.34	2.19	2.03	1.95	1.86	1.76	1.66	1.53	1.38
∞	6.63	4.61	3.78	3.32	3.02	2.80	2.64	2.51	2.41	2.32	2.18	2.04	1.88	1.79	1.70	1.59	1.47	1.32	1.00

Degrees of freedom for denominator

* This table is reproduced from M. Merrington and C. M. Thompson, "Tables of percentage points of the inverted beta (F) distribution,"

To illustrate the use of Table V, suppose that in a random sample of 250 cigarette smokers there were 60 who preferred Brand A and 190 who preferred some other brand. It is desired to obtain a confidence interval for the true proportion of smokers preferring Brand A. The sample proportion of smokers preferring Brand A being $60/250 = 0.24$, one begins by marking this value on the horizontal scale, the x/n scale, of Table V. Since $n = 250$, one then goes up *vertically* from this point until one reaches the two curves labeled 250. The values of the vertical scale that correspond to the points at which these two curves are thus cut give the desired confidence limits for the true proportion. For $x/n = 60/250 = 0.24$ they are, roughly, 0.19 and 0.30 and one can assert with a probability of 0.95 that the interval from 0.19 to 0.30 contains the true proportion of smokers preferring Brand A to all other brands of cigarettes.

Table V. 95% Confidence Intervals for Proportions*

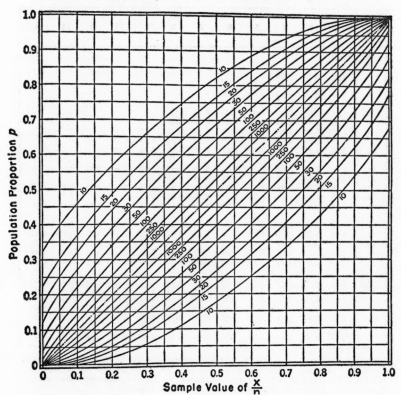

* This table is reproduced from C. J. Clopper and E. S. Pearson, "The use of confidence or fiducial limits illustrated in the case of the binomial," *Biometrika*, Vol. 26 (1934), by permission of the *Biometrika* trustees.

Table VI. Values of r_p for the New Multiple Range Test*

d.f. \ p	2	3	4	5	6	7	8	9	10	12	14	16
1	17.97											
2	6.09	6.09										
3	4.50	4.52	4.52									
4	3.93	4.01	4.03	4.03								
5	3.64	3.75	3.80	3.81	3.81							
6	3.46	3.59	3.65	3.68	3.69	3.70						
7	3.34	3.48	3.55	3.59	3.61	3.62	3.63					
8	3.26	3.40	3.48	3.52	3.55	3.57	3.57	3.58				
9	3.20	3.34	3.42	3.47	3.50	3.52	3.54	3.54	3.55			
10	3.15	3.29	3.38	3.43	3.47	3.49	3.51	3.52	3.52			
11	3.11	3.26	3.34	3.40	3.44	3.46	3.48	3.49	3.50	3.51		
12	3.08	3.23	3.31	3.37	3.41	3.44	3.46	3.47	3.48	3.50		
13	3.06	3.20	3.29	3.35	3.39	3.42	3.44	3.46	3.47	3.48	3.49	
14	3.03	3.18	3.27	3.33	3.37	3.40	3.43	3.44	3.46	3.47	3.48	
15	3.01	3.16	3.25	3.31	3.36	3.39	3.41	3.43	3.45	3.47	3.48	3.48
16	3.00	3.14	3.23	3.30	3.34	3.38	3.40	3.42	3.44	3.46	3.47	3.48
17	2.98	3.13	3.22	3.28	3.33	3.37	3.39	3.41	3.43	3.45	3.46	3.47
18	2.97	3.12	3.21	3.27	3.32	3.36	3.38	3.40	3.42	3.44	3.46	3.47
19	2.96	3.11	3.20	3.26	3.31	3.35	3.38	3.40	3.41	3.44	3.46	3.47
20	2.95	3.10	3.19	3.25	3.30	3.34	3.37	3.39	3.41	3.43	3.45	3.46
24	2.92	3.07	3.16	3.23	3.28	3.31	3.35	3.37	3.39	3.42	3.44	3.45
30	2.89	3.03	3.13	3.20	3.25	3.29	3.32	3.35	3.37	3.40	3.43	3.45
40	2.86	3.01	3.10	3.17	3.22	3.27	3.30	3.33	3.35	3.39	3.42	3.44
60	2.83	2.98	3.07	3.14	3.20	3.24	3.28	3.31	3.33	3.37	3.40	3.43
120	2.80	2.95	3.04	3.12	3.17	3.22	3.25	3.29	3.31	3.36	3.39	3.42
∞	2.77	2.92	3.02	3.09	3.15	3.19	3.23	3.27	3.29	3.34	3.38	3.41

* This table is reproduced from H. L. Harter, "Critical values for Duncan's new multiple range test." It contains some corrected values to replace those given by D. B. Duncan in "Multiple Range and Multiple F Tests," *Biometrics*, Vol. 11, 1955. The above table is reproduced with the permission of the author and the editor of *Biometrics*.